ISLANDS OF ANGRY GHOSTS

HUGH EDWARDS

ISLANDS OF ANGRY GHOSTS

Angus&Robertson
An imprint of HarperCollins*Publishers*

Angus&Robertson
An imprint of the HarperCollins*Publishers,* Australia

First published in London by Hodder & Stoughton Ltd in 1966
A&R paperback edition first published in 1973
Reprinted in 1974, 1975, 1977, 1979, 1985
This A&R paperback edition 1989
Reprinted in 1991, 1993, 1994, 1996, 1998, 1999
by HarperCollins*Publishers* Pty Limited
ACN 009 913 517
A member of the HarperCollins*Publishers* (Australia) Pty Limited Group
http://www.harpercollins.com.au

HarperCollins*Publishers*
25 Ryde Road, Pymble, Sydney, NSW 2073, Australia
31 View Road, Glenfield, Auckland 10, New Zealand
77-85 Fulham Palace Road, London W6 8JB, United Kingdom
Hazelton Lanes, 55 Avenue Road, Suite 2900, Toronto, Ontario M5R 3L2
and 1995 Markham Road, Scarborough, Ontario M1B 5M8, Canada
10 East 53rd Street, New York NY 10022, USA

National Library of Australia Cataloguing-in-Publication data:

Edwards, Hugh, 1933– .
Islands of angry ghosts.
Bibliography
Includes index
ISBN 0 207 16317 0.
1. Batavia (Ship). 2. Shipwreck – Western Australia. I. Title.
919.41'04

Printed in Australia by Griffin Press Pty Ltd on 80gsm Econoprint

16 15 14 13 99 00 01 02

CONTENTS

This book is for the
memory of Maurie Hammond, who
loved life, people, and old
shipwrecks.

The author wishes to thank the
late Henrietta Drake-Brockman
for permission to use excerpts
from Francisco Pelsart's
journals, translated for her by
Mr E. D. Drok of Perth from
microfilm of the original in the
Algemeen Rijksarchief in
the Netherlands.

The full text of the
journals may be found in
Mrs Drake-Brockman's book
Voyage to Disaster,
Angus & Robertson, Sydney 1963.

PART ONE

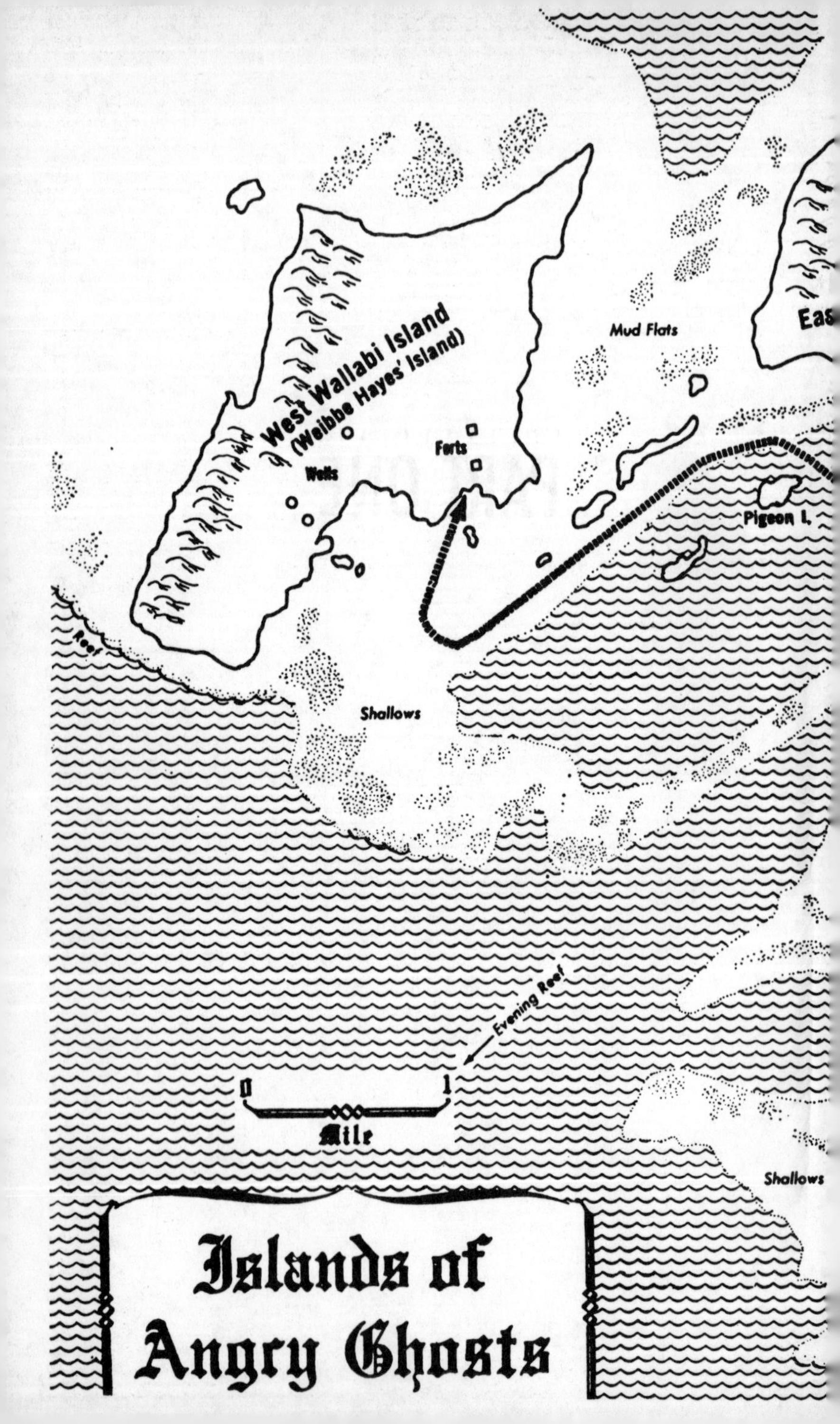

West Wallabi Island
(Weibbe Hayes' Island)
Wells
Forts
Mud Flats
Pigeon I.
Reef
Shallows
Evening Reef
0
1
Mile
Shallows
Islands of Angry Ghosts

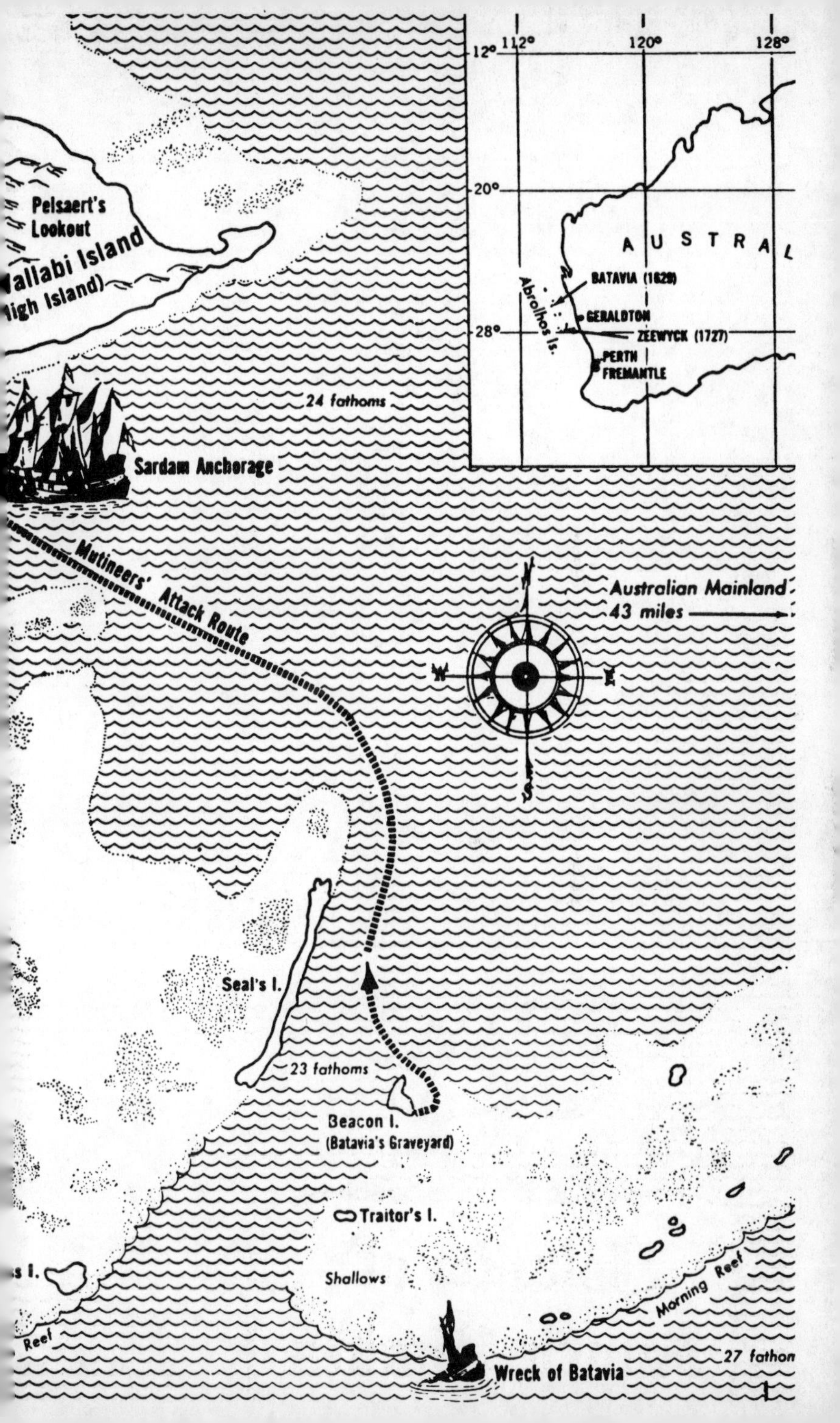

112°
120°
128°
12°
20°
28°
A U S T R A L
BATAVIA (1629)
Abrolhos Is.
GERALDTON
ZEEWYCK (1727)
PERTH
FREMANTLE
Pelsaert's
Lookout
Wallabi Island
(High Island)
24 fathoms
Sardam Anchorage
Mutineers' Attack Route
Australian Mainland
43 miles
N
W
E
S
Seal's I.
23 fathoms
Beacon I.
(Batavia's Graveyard)
Traitor's I.
Shallows
Reef
Morning Reef
27 fathom
Wreck of Batavia

1 , YELLOW BONES OF MURDER

"Murdered," said George Brenzi.

It was obvious enough. A glance at the skeleton in the shallow coral island grave—even before we found the sword cleft in the skull—showed that the man had not died a natural death. The backward twist of the head with the jawbone fixed in a gruesome laughing yawn, and the legs and arms obscenely sprawled told their own story.

Our expedition doctor, Naoom Haimson, was specific. He diagnosed death from a cut throat after the man had been felled by cutlass blows.

They made a strange contrast: the modern diver-medico in faded blue trousers and cotton shirt, and the yellow skeleton of a man murdered by mutineers on this island three centuries ago. The rest of us were standing awkwardly about, more accustomed to diving below the waves than digging up old graves in dusty soil.

Rivulets of coral sand trickled back into the grave as Doc squatted on the edge, squinting through the smoke from his old black pipe.

"A tall fellow," he said. "Over six feet, and from the condition of the teeth and the lines on the skull, quite young. I should think less than twenty." He pointed with the stem of his pipe. "You can see how they got him. He was probably running away and the first cutlass blow caught him on the right shoulder from behind. It broke or severed the shoulder at the scapula and the second blow cut into the skull, inflicting a slight depressed fracture and probably stunning him. At least I hope so."

"Why?" asked George.

"Because then they cut his throat so savagely it disarticulated the jawbone," Doc finished quietly.

We made wry grimaces. The mutineers from the Dutch East India Company vessel *Batavia,* wrecked on a nearby reef, had been very fond of cutting throats.

This island, a mere platform of sand and coral slabs and quite unremarkable in all other respects, had seen such an incredible series of violent and bloody incidents during a few months of the year 1629, it had gained a permanent niche of notoriety in Australian history. *"Het Eylandt van Bataviaes Kerkhof* . . . the island of Batavia's graveyard," the Dutch castaways had called it. An expressive name, for it became a graveyard of men as well.

And this was why we were here. We had come to dive for the wreck of the *Batavia,* and to reconstruct the events of the 1629 shipwreck, mutiny and murders—land and undersea archaeology.

At first, looking around at the featureless island—treeless, smaller than a football field, with its four northward-facing fishermen's huts, the three jetties spider-legging south out over the coral shallows—we had found it hard to imagine in 1963 that this was really the place where it all happened.

Until we looked down at the drop-jawed skeleton again.

Then it was not so difficult to picture the mutineers' leader, Jeronimus Cornelisz, strutting these few miserable acres of sand, resplendent in his scarlet coat with its gold trimmings, the power of life and death in his elegant gesture. Or to see in imagination the murderers with their swords parading before their *bijwijven*—women who spent their sad-faced days sitting outside the tents erected from wreck sails and spars among the bushes, waiting for the mutineers' foetid pleasure. These female passengers were faced with this degraded and carnal existence as the only alternative to having their throats slit. The other women, men, children—even infants in arms—were killed by Cornelisz' bloodthirsty and sadistic ruffians.

Cornelisz reigned here for the brief lifetime of one of the island's winter daisies, lording it arrogantly with his mutineer bodyguard and the jewels and money they could not spend. He was emperor over two acres of sand, the numbers of his fascinated but fearful subjects dwindling as he had them murdered, one by one.

We leaned on our shovels.

"It would be interesting to hold a conversation with him," George said, looking down on our skeleton, "and find out just what did happen here."

The skull laughed up at him.

Andries de Vries was a tall, aesthetic youth, not quite twenty when he signed to become a clerk with the Dutch East India Company in 1628, fired by the tales he had read and heard of the romantic East. When he boarded the *Batavia* with her gay flags and pennants at Amsterdam in October that year, it seemed the start of a great adventure, and his boy's mind was filled with visions of coconut palms, flaming volcanoes, heathen temples, and dancing native maidens with bare, firm breasts.

Instead he found shipwreck and these gray, miserable, wind-blasted Abrolhos Islands. The dream became a nightmare of chaos, confusion, and people dying of thirst, hunger, and loss of heart around him. Then mutiny, and the grinning fiends taking him by the arm and dragging him to the raft on the beach.

There were two other men there, both pale and frightened. They could smell evil, but without swords they were powerless to resist and so they boarded the raft and sat meekly but wide-eyed and staring about them, while four mutineers poled the craft away across the shallows toward the other islands.

At Traitor's Island they learned the truth: They were to be drowned. Their pleas and protestations were in vain. The mutineers threw them roughly to the ground, trussed their arms and legs with ropes so tightly that their limbs ached, and carried them one by one into the shallows where they drowned helplessly with threshings and bubblings. Andries was the last.

He wept and pleaded for his life, groveling on the coral stones at their feet. They had just killed two men, and the boy moved a little pity in their hearts—they were not hardened to killing yet, as they would be later—and so they let him live. But they devised a special task for him, and Andries de Vries soon found he had bought his own life at the price of others.

"Andries," said Jeronimus Cornelisz a few days later, "in the infirmary tent there are eleven sick people. They are useless to our purpose, incumbents. In any case they will probably die and it would be kinder to kill them quickly. Here is a sharp knife, Andries. Cut their throats and prove your friendship for us."

So began the agony of Andries de Vries. When he had washed the blood from his hands, weeping silently in case they should hear him, he knew his own days were numbered. He could never be a pirate. He was not cruel enough and they would find him out and purge him . . . and no amount of seawater and sand could ever wash away the memory of those sick, their dead eyes staring reproachfully. Even for his own life the price was too great.

God—Why haven't I the courage to refuse them and die like a man? he asked himself, knowing the answer.

When they called him again, on July 13, his stomach turned to water and his knees shook, but he accepted the knife without argument. "Kill the remaining sick, Andries," said Cornelisz with a strange glitter in his eyes, polishing his nails under the silk trappings in the big tent. *"Vermood ze!"*

He did.

Next day, eyes red-rimmed pits of horror, he confessed to Lucretia van der Mylen. She was his only friend on the island, but even her beautiful face showed revulsion. *"Nee Andries!* I couldn't believe it of you!" Tormented, he turned away.

De Vries had signed his death sentence. Jeronimus Cornelisz had forbidden the rank and file to talk to Lucretia, his concubine who would find her own self-reproach later. Andries had been seen and the spy hurried to Cornelisz' tent, filled with the riches looted from the ship.

"Captain-General . . . !"

"He has served his purpose," said Jeronimus grimly, putting down the carafe of wine. "Send me Rutger Fredericx, Jan Hendricx, and Lenert Michielsz van Os." He opened the chest in which the swords were kept.

A few minutes later the three emerged from the tent, wiping wine from their beards. Lenert Michielsz slashed the air with his sword, and the noon sun glinted on the blade.

"Andries!" he called mockingly. Lucretia hid her face. "Come here, Andries!"

De Vries fled in terror, his long awkward legs stumbling and slipping on the coral flags. Behind him came the murderers, laughing, unhurried. Soon enough de Vries reached the end of the island. . . .

Now, three centuries later in July, 1963, his bones, uncovered by our shovels, still carried the horror of his death.

How the world had changed, I thought standing there, since a midwife slapped sharply to make him suck the first mewing, protesting breath of life in old Amsterdam so long ago. On that day of his birth Queen Elizabeth was barely dead, Drake had gone to a sea grave not many years before, buccaneers were in their heydey on the Spanish Main, Shakespeare was still joking with Ben Johnson over ale in London taverns, and Australia was yet undiscovered.

In our dead man's time galleons, rolling keel-heavy across the oceans, buffeted by storms, mirrored in calms, desiccated by sickness, sometimes took a year to make the journey from Europe, and arrived with only half their complements. I could have boarded a KLM aircraft at Schipol Airport near Amsterdam, or a Qantas airliner in London, and reached the same destination with a whine of jet engines after twenty hours of reading glossy magazines, eating chicken sandwiches, and sipping King George scotch and soda, peering out and down through the clouds just occasionally to watch the world slip past below.

But for all our engineering miracles—automobiles, space rockets, telephones, television, the big blue Evinrude outboards and silver Airdive underwater breathing apparatus brought on our expedition to search for the wreck of the *Batavia* in her coral seagrave—for all these things, Andries de Vries had been born a creature of flesh and blood like ourselves. He'd had a few more superstitions and fears, perhaps; less mechanical know-how; hadn't been as solid in the tooth from bad diet and lack of a dentist. But he'd been a human being of similar size, stature, appearance, and sensitivity. The coral would have hurt his feet just as it did ours; the wind would have made him shiver, the sun warmed him; the acrid odor of fish cooking over coals would have smelled as good to him as it did to us. And in those final moments of horror we would have been no less terrified than he was. The thought of the sun-glinting cutlasses made my scalp prickle and my throat go dry. . . .

We stood around the grave silently, twentieth-century explorers, each man thinking of a death, the cold Abrolhos wind riffling our shirts, and the dead man stirring our thoughts.

My mind went back to a time long ago. The time when it all began.

2 SHIP ON THE BRINK OF MUTINY

She was a ship balanced on the sword-edge of mutiny on that last evening, June 3, 1629.

There was no outward sign of the catastrophe to come. On the contrary it was a treacherously sweet night as she dipped her red lion figurehead on a Northeast course through the long swells of the Indian Ocean toward the fatal point of time and place waiting for her below the horizon. Her mastheads swung in gentle arcs across the early stars, a warm breeze filled the sails, and the phosphorescent wake stretched back toward Africa. "All's well!" cried the provost at the turn of the watch, striking the mainmast ceremoniously with his mace.

But below decks evil suppurated. As the ship rolled eastward from the Cape of Good Hope, a dozen men had been meeting furtively in a dark lower-deck cabin to plan a mutiny and the murder of most of the 316 people aboard. Now their swords were sharp and ready, and they itched to use them.

The *Batavia* would be a rich prize. She was the newest and finest ship in the Indies fleet, heavy-bellied with cargo, carrying besides cloth, wines, cheeses, and trade goods, twelve bound chests of heavy silver coin worth 250,000 guilders, as well as a casket of jewels worth a mogul's ransom. And once they had taken her they could become richer still by pirating under the pretense of the Dutch East India Company flag. It would be a year or more before she was reported missing. Meantime they could trap and prey on sister ships like a cannibal fish, looting, burning, cutting throats, multiplying their wealth until they could match their own gross weights in gold, silver, and gems. This was their dream of greed. And on this night the plan was ripe.

The common folk aboard ship had no inkling that they were about to take part in history. They believed that they were ordinary people aboard an ordinary ship, due to make a Java landfall within the month after thirty-two weary weeks at sea. Their destination was the port of Batavia (present-day Jakarta) after which their ship had been named in Amsterdam. Already in their imaginations they could smell the musk of the tropics and hear the rustle of coconut palms. Some of the passengers taking the night air on deck speculated excitedly about the new country, and some—in the way of people who have been too long at sea—grumbled about the ship.

"*Ach!* It will be so good to stretch your legs on dry land again," sighed stout Anneken Hardens, resting her ample posterior against a gun carriage. "To be able to walk twenty steps in a straight line without falling over ropes or into the sea . . . And the food tonight! It was uneatable. Packed like salt herrings we are, into the guts of this gilded barge. A painted pigsty! I pray every day to see land."

She was ungrateful. The *Batavia* was no barge but the most magnificent ship of her time to sail to the Indies. The Spaniards may have built ships bigger, but no shipwrights ever built them better than the Dutch. They worked the best seasoned Baltic oak to make the stoutest vessels afloat. *Batavia* was not small even by modern standards. She was three times the size of Columbus's two smaller vessels, twice the size of Bligh's *Bounty* or Cook's *Endeavour*. She was about 140 feet in length, 40 feet in the beam, and 40 feet from deck to keel—as wooden ships went, a considerable craft. She carried 600 tons of cargo, and found cramped space for more than 300 soldiers, passengers, and crew below decks.

Like most of the Dutch East India Company *retour* vessels * which spent their working lives at sea, plying between Holland and the islands of the Far East (often taking four years on the return trip), she was magnificently decorated. Her scrolled and carved hull was lavishly painted green and gold, the lion-of-Holland figurehead, snarling in perpetual rage at the waves ahead, was daubed bright scarlet, and her

* A *retour* vessel was one engaged on a "return" voyage, as distinct from haphazard or opportunistic trading. The Dutch still use the expression today.

towering spread of sail, as yet undarkened by salt, retained the virgin whiteness of the day she left Amsterdam as flagship of the Indies fleet, with all her pennants flying. Few ships have been prettier than the *Batavia* on her tragic voyage.

Living conditions below decks were another thing. Even on a flagship they were something to be endured with prayer and fortitude after the best part of a year at sea. Bedding was filthy, green scum and indescribable things floated in the water barrels, the salt meat was rotting, there were weevils in the biscuits, everyone had the itch, some had boils, a few had scurvy. But that was the way of all ships of the time, and even admirals had to put up with maggots in their food.

Nevertheless *Batavia* was better than most, and if Annie Hardens and some of the other grumblers had been aboard the *Dordrecht* or the other long-service ships of the fleet, they really would have had something to wail about: leaks, mould, damp rot, rats, and bugs that came out of the wood at night to suck blood. But the *Dordrecht* was at least to reach her Java port. While the clear and delicate notes of the plucked lute wafted across the *Batavia's* deck that night and laughter drifted free, death was waiting for most of the passengers—including Anneken Hardens, who would regret her prayers about seeing land.

In a dark cabin in the steerage, where the creaking of the rudder post could clearly be heard, and a single flickering candle threw monstrous shadows on the tarred oaken walls, the conspirators were meeting again—the Devil's brethren, *muyters,* nervous-eyed and furtive as bats. They arrived cloaked and singly, looking back over their shoulders, talking in sibilant whispers, one of them always watching through a knot in the door lest they should be overheard and betrayed.

The recital began like a litany; they had been through it many times.

"*Als we de Kust van het Zuydlandt zien* . . . when we sight the Southland coast!" the first one breathed, making the cutthroat sign across his jugular with a grimy, crooked forefinger.

His neighbor nodded. "Stick Commander Pelsaert with a yard of cold steel through his white breast. Pin him to his bunk and blanket. Throw him in his blood and nightshirt through the gilt stern windows to the sharks waiting below."

"Nail down the hatch of the soldiers' quarters for'ard so that they buzz in there li e wasps in a corked bottle. Pluck their strings from them later," s the next man. "They will join us to save their lives."

"*Ja!* An are masters of the ship, the money, and the jewels!"

Together the voices began to rise in hoarse excitement.

"Women and children over the side. Splash! To the sharks. Hags and brats—except for the pretty girls. We'll keep the coquettes to while away the tropic nights . . . aaah!"

"Make the officers walk the plank—see how high and mighty they are then. The bastards . . . !"

"And steer for the Malacca coast, and Coromandel, and Madagascar. To pick off the Company's ships like plump silly ducks until the word gets out. Then back to quit the loot on the Barbary Coast while the men-o'war grow weed on their keels and worms in their hulls criss-crossing the southern oceans looking for us, snug back home. To live for the rest of our lives as rich men. With wine and white bread, and white linen, and servants, and more money and better ways to spend it than all these fat merchants with their snivelling manner and parsimonious honesty. Ho!"

Glasses clinked and fumes of *genever* gin and rank wine filled the rathole cabin. They had a right to be confident.

Like all ships of her day the *Batavia* was stoutly armed against pirates and potential foes. She carried twenty-eight cannon, seven of them great bronze pieces, a company of soldiers, as well as an arsenal with arms for every able-bodied man aboard. And Dutch merchantmen by custom traveled to the Indies in convoy, with fast flute ships and a hulking ship of war to guard the merchantmen. For any vessel short of a man-o-war, she would be a tough nut to crack.

But there was a chink in the armor. As with the ancient city of Troy, provision had not been made for an attack from *inside* the great wooden fortresses. The ship's arms and routine were ordered in such a way that a handful of crew members by a bold bid at the ripe time, could take the vessel by surprise and achieve by cunning what a large, well-armed craft could not do by force and much shedding of blood.

It was a hard and cruel age. Mutiny was by no means uncommon and piracy on the high seas was a profitable and widely practiced profession. Perhaps the great Dutch East India Company should have made further provision against its own soldiers and sailors succumbing to the temptations of the rich cargoes aboard East Indies ships. But the *Batavia* was a precedent. In thirty years of sailing to the Indies nothing like it had happened before. The Dutch had so long prided themselves on their discipline, common sense, and God-fearing honesty, that the news of the mutiny came as a shock like a clout from a mizzen block to everyone from the Governor-General of Batavia downward. The most bitter part of the pill that the authorities had to swallow later was that the principal instigators of the plot on the *Batavia* were the skipper, Ariaen Jacobsz, and the undermerchant, Jeronimus Cornelisz, the two most senior men on the vessel after Commandeur Francisco Pelsaert himself. And both of these trusted servants of the Company were backed and aided in their crime by young nobility—the cadets or junior officers—not mere discontented rabble from the common hands, which would have been more comprehensible.

The plot was conceived with cunning, and was well concealed on the long run across the Indian Ocean from the Cape of Good Hope. No one outside the immediate circle of conspirators—and certainly not Pelsaert himself—had an inkling of what was intended. Fear of death and worse made the plotters as cautious as night-hunting spiders. The punishments for mutiny were terrible. If a whisper escaped, the very kindest fate they could expect was to be publicly hanged in chains on the gibbet outside the Castle of Batavia and left to dangle as a warning to others until they became sun-blackened husks. It was more likely that the judges, scowling under their tall black hats, would order something like breaking while spread-eagled on a wheel—bones large and small from the toes and fingers inward to the trunk, pulp-broken with a metal rod while the crowd watched and savored until death came in the end as a sweet relief. That was more the measure of mutineers.

So the plot on the *Batavia,* born of the discontents and evil ambitions of skipper Ariaen Jacobsz and Jeronimus Cornelisz, nurtured on the destructive sex and sadistic impulses of the cadets, and fattened by circumstance, matured slowly and carefully. The inner circle of villains by sly suggestion and intrigue attracted others to their cause in secret cells so that no one knew who or how many men were implicated.

Recruiting the brute sword-swinging strength of common hands was not difficult, since every Indiaman carried her share of rabble from the brothels and taverns of Amsterdam among her soldiers and sailors; men who would slit their mothers' throats for a piece of eight, let alone a share in 250,000 guilders.

The plan itself was quite simple. The first step was to separate *Batavia* from the rest of the fleet and especially to lose the watchful man-o'-war *Buren* with her three decks of guns. Skipper Ariaen Jacobsz accomplished this in storms south of the Cape of Good Hope, and no one was any the wiser—storms had often separated ships before.

"No matter," Commandeur Pelsaert said, more disturbed about the loss of the convoy than he cared to admit. "As God wills. We may come up with them again in higher latitudes."

Jacobsz made sure they did not.

The next move was to undermine Commandeur Pelsaert's position of authority aboard. For a time he was so ill south of Cabo de Bona Esperanza that the mutineers hoped fervently for his death. But he disappointed them by recovering, and so they began a subversive whispering campaign against him, slandering his relations with one of the attractive young women passengers, Lucretia van der Mylen. They decided to provoke him into unpopular disciplinary measures.

Jacobsz and Cornelisz had their chief tool, the High Boatswain Jan Evertsz, organize a group of his men to make a shocking and disgusting attack on the lady. They pounced on her at dusk in a companionway, stifling her screams. Silent, sweating men with a grim intensity of purpose, they stripped her naked, half-strangled her with her own hair ribbon, and smeared her body and face with excreta and black pitch, leaving her sobbing and hysterical on the deck for the outraged officer of the watch to find.

As expected, Pelsaert choked with fury when he heard and ordered a full investigation. The crooked answers and averted eyes during his inquiries disturbed Pelsaert. During his weeks of sickness he had lost touch with the mood of the ship. He knew that Skipper Jacobsz hated him heartily and he knew also that Jacobsz' big-breasted lover, Zwaantie Hendrix (who was sleeping with him to the scandal of the ship), had begun the voyage as Lucretia's serving maid and now loathed her former mistress and would do anything to spite her. But these were suspicions. The only name he could get in direct evidence was that of the High Boatswain, Jan Evertsz. Lucretia had recognized his voice in the darkness during the attack.

Pelsaert was reluctant to have any unpleasantness on board that might stand to his discredit when they reached Java. Ships under good commanders made smooth passages. But the incident involving Lucretia van der Mylen was of such a serious nature that he was compelled to make some disciplinary move. The sternly Protestant Dutch regarded sex offenses as hanging matters, and so he decided that when they sighted the Australian coast he would accuse Evertsz and have him put in chains. They would be less than a fortnight's sail from Batavia

Castle then, and the scar-faced high boatswain could be turned over bound to the V.O.C. fiscal advocates or public prosecutors. Under torture (and they were very efficient at that in Batavia Castle) he might reveal the names of his accomplices. At any rate it would be out of Pelsaert's hands.

Unkown to him this arrest was just what the mutineers desired. When Evertsz had been put in chains they planned to stir up feeling against Pelsaert, saying that they "would not let innocent men hang on the false testimony of whores and adulterers." There is no evidence that Lucretia was ever anything of the sort, but her friendliness with Pelsaert would work against them both, and during the doubt and confusion created in people's minds, the mutineers would seize their opportunity, and take over the ship during the night watch. With half the officers and cadets implicated, they reasoned that they would not be opposed by the bewildered common people. They must succeed.

"God himself could not prevent our success," boasted Ariaen Jacobsz blasphemously over a mug of gin on that last evening.

Pelsaert would later claim that the wreck was an Act of God conceived because the Creator was so outraged at the villainies outlined in the mutiny plot that "Rather He let the ship be wrecked."

On that night of June 3, the plotters met in the steerage cabin. Pelsaert lay ill once more in his bunk, beset by doubts and torments; Lucretia van der Mylen was weeping in her bed, wishing the nightmare voyage over and herself reunited with her husband, Boudewyn, already in Java; Ariaen Jacobsz was striding arrogantly in high seaboots and cloak to take command of the night watch. Disaster lay just over the horizon; the great Southland, sleeping like a tawny lion in the east, was closer than anyone imagined.

Between the Australian coast and the unheeding vessel lay the white, wraithlike islands of the Abrolhos archipelago. . . a ship death trap. So low they were hard to see in daylight from any distance, they were invisible at night. Surrounded by reefs, currents, great waves breaking, the storm-swept home of gull and crab, they crouched flat on the sea like grey cats, ready to flick out their claws and rake the bottom out of a passing ship. At midnight *Batavia* was already passing the first of the reefs, barely a couple of miles to starboard, a great flat reef which the seas pounded in fury—a portion of the archipelago later to be called the Easter Group of islands. The wind blew the thunder of the surf away toward land and no one heard it. Jacobsz once stirred uneasily and focused his telescope in its direction in the darkness but, seeing nothing, he put the telescope away.

The *Batavia* sailed on her doomed course. A fraction to port, or quarter of a mile to starboard, and she would have sailed unknowing through the islands and sighted the Southland at noon the next day. But Fate had not planned it that way, and her reef was waiting.

Four hours to go. . . .

3 PRELUDE TO DISASTER

On that last night before the wreck, sleepless beneath his blanket in the lonely vault of the ship's great cabin, Commandeur Francisco Pelsaert churned with doubts, indecision, perhaps forboding. The gods who once made him a favorite had now turned thier faces from him.

At the time of his departure from Holland seven months before, he was the envy of all his contemporaries: commandeur of a splendid ship, President of the Fleet, on his way to becoming a member of the Council of India . . . In ten short years he had risen from the rank of humble clerk to the post of senior and most powerful executive with future fame and fortune seemingly a foregone conclusion. Now, in a few hours, he would face the crisis of his life.

Perhaps as he tossed in his bunk he was remembering that old quarrel at Surat. Or perhaps he was thinking of Lucretia van der Mylen.

We have no physical description of Francisco Pelsaert, but there is a portrait copied from an etching or engraving supposedly made in India about 1625; its origin is obscure. But it is a portrait of a man in the post-Elizabethan style—long hair, flared moustache, Shakespeare beard, high white collar, padded doublet, with a medallion around his neck. It is much like any one of thousands of similar portraits of the period. But the face, looked at apart from the fashions of the time, is interesting. There is a high, intelligent forehead, wide-set eyes with a thoughtful, rather gentle expression, and a slightly aquiline nose. The expression of the mouth is pleasant, the lips concise. The impression one gains is of a man of about thirty-five, neat and dapper in appearance, intelligent and tolerant in outlook, efficient in operation, but a man of effective thoughts and letters rather than action. As other guides we have his handwriting and the views expressed in his journals. Both of these tend to confirm the analysis.

Francisco Pelsaert was born in Antwerp and appears to have inherited the Flemish flair for business rather than the stolid Dutch method of system. He joined the Dutch East India Company, the de Vereenighde Oost-Indische Compagnie (or V.O.C. as its clerks wrote it, to save scratching quills over all those unwieldy syllables), in 1618. He was then in his twenties and probably signed at the instigation of his brother-in-law, Hendrik Brouwer, a famous V.O.C. admiral.

Pelsaert's rapid rise during succeeding years illustrated his obvious ability. He was sent to the Indies as a matter of natural course and three years later was an undermerchant (in the Company system of ranking), at 55 guilders per month. When he left India to return to Holland in 1627, he was an uppermerchant at a vastly increased salary. And when he sailed again to the Indies aboard the *Batavia* in 1628, he was President of the Fleet, and a commandeur—the most senior V.O.C. rank—receiving probably 200 guilders per month. A common seaman or soldier of the time received less than 10. All this in ten years. Obviously Pelsaert was an exceptional executive and the Dutch, quick to recognize profit or merit, had appreciated his qualities and shown their appreciation in his rapid promotion.

His principal success occurred during a period at the Court of the Mogul Prince Jahangir, in northern India, where he had been sent to pursue the indigo trade (indigo being much in demand in Europe at the time for dyeing the stout woolen cloth called *laken,* used by the stout merchants in their respectable suiting). Not only did he produce an eminently satisfactory trade balance, he produced a report suggesting certain trade reforms and systems which pleased his superiors mightily.

His report influenced them to promote him and persuade him to return to India against his earlier declared intentions. (When he quit Agra in 1627 to go back to Holland, he had said fervently that he would never return again to that sun-sucked, fevered land.) Health was the reason. Many V.O.C. men had found lonely graves in eastern countries and the death rate was appalling. Malaria and dysentery were the chief killers, but smallpox, cholera, typhoid, leprosy, and yellow fever welcomed white men with equal enthusiasm.

Pelsaert had been sick—probably with malaria—and it had frightened him. Besides, India had a wretched steam-bath climate for a white man. "This would be a desirable country," he wrote in his report, "if men might indulge their hunger or appetite as they do in our cold lands; but the excessive heat makes a man powerless, takes away his desire for food, and limits him to water-drinking which weakens or debilitates the body. . . ."

He left, not intending to return.

By one of those twists of life, the skipper of the ship which was to carry Pelsaert back to Holland was Ariaen Jacobsz.

In the harbor of Surat, waiting to sail, Pelsaert and Jacobsz quarreled violently. Jacobsz was reprimanded by two senior V.O.C. officers, Commandeur Grijph and Uppermerchant Gheleijnsen, who said that this "was not the manner in which to sail to the Fatherland," and that "He [Jacobsz] must behave himself differently toward [Pelsaert] . . ."

Jacobsz shut his mouth. But he did not forgive or forget.

Neither he nor Pelsaert could have guessed that less than a year later Jacobsz, appointed skipper of the new ship *Batavia,* would find himself linked again with Pelsaert, now greatly elevated and his superior officer. The spite of Surat was to be reawakened with increased venom and calamitous consequences.

Pelsaert spent only four months in Holland. It is probable that his brother-in-law, Hendrik Brouwer (now one of the directors and a powerful voice in the East India Company), was pleased with his India report. Perhaps he pressed for his brother-in-law's promotion, and persuaded him to return to the tropics before his damaged health was really ready for it. At any rate Pelsaert changed his mind, and when the *Batavia,* flying her gay pennants and bright flags, sailed from Amsterdam on her maiden voyage October 27, 1628, she was flagship of the fleet, and Pelsaert her commandeur and fleet president.

Among his possessions Francisco Pelsaert carried a letter from the High and Mighty Seventeen (directors of the V.O.C.), recommending him in the highest terms to Governor General Jan Pieters Coen in Batavia: "Because we have heard very good reports of his previous services we therefore recommend him to your Honour, hereby asking you to keep in mind his person and to note future services . . . and advance the said Pelsaert . . . to such positions as his conduct and quality shall merit." Pelsaert, in 1628, was an executive of ability and promise, and he was clearly favored in the eyes of his superiors.

He stepped aboard the *Batavia* not as a captain nor an admiral but a merchant. It was common V.O.C. practice to place landsmen, senior merchants, in charge of their trading vessels. Commandeur was their title in this supervisory role. The actual navigation and sailing from point to point (under due direction) was carried out by the skippers.

Ariaen Jacobsz, whose faulty navigation was to cause the wreck of the *Batavia,* was Pelsaert's mortal enemy. They were opposites in character, physique, and temperament. Jacobsz was a big-fisted, raw-Dutch, hard-drinking, brawling, braggadocio; Pelsaert a fine-boned man of small stature, rather artistically inclined, a friend of artists such as Rubens, the great Flemish painter. Jacobsz was necessarily a good seaman because he was promoted from the lumbering *Dordrecht* (the vessel from which the Abrolhos were first sighted in 1619 by Frederik de Houtman) to the brand new *Batavia,* finest ship in the Indies fleet. But from all accounts he was a choleric captain. Flinging blistering oaths at slight provocation, hard on his men, harboring grudges, he was as tough and weather-beaten as an Indiaman's mainmast spar.

He and Pelsaert were dissimilar in almost every respect—each the type of man the other most detested. To say that they were incompatible would be an understatement; cooped up together on a ship the personality mixture was downright explosive. The trouble which began at Surat was inflamed by an unsuccessful infatuation Jacobsz had for Lucretia van der Mylen at the beginning of the voyage. That she was more inclined to the cultured and lively personality of Francisco Pelsaert we do not know for certain, but it seems likely—and it would be another reason for Jacobsz to hate Pelsaert's guts.

At the Cape of Good Hope, after weeks of forced politeness and words gritted through clenched teeth, there came the inevitable open rift between commandeur and skipper. While the vessel was in Table Bay revictualing and Pelsaert was absent seeing to the supplies, scowling Jacobsz, sick of what he regarded as prissy primness, ripped off his starched collar and captain's manners, and went on a jagged drinking bout among the other ships of the fleet. He was accompanied by Undermerchant Jeronimus Cornelisz and Lucretia's maidservant, Zwaantie Hendrix, whom shipboard rumor had it "refused the skipper nothing."

Jacobsz had been a renowned drinker in his days as high boatswain on the *Berger Boot,* and the raw *genever* gin (a favorite among the seamen) was nectar to his leather throat and balm to his bruised pride. As Jacobsz got drunker, his language and temper grew fouler. Wherever he went he said indiscreet things about Pelsaert. He scandalized the crew of the *Sardam,* and on board the warship *Buren* he became enthusiastically involved in an open brawl, damaging a number of her crew and behaving "Very beastly with words as well as deeds."

Next day the commanders of the *Sardam* and *Buren* sent stiff notes to Pelsaert protesting Jacobsz' behavior. Perhaps if Pelsaert had been more human that day with the skipper (who knew well enough that he had behaved badly) disaster might have been averted, even at this late stage. But Pelsaert, with barbed words, spared his old enemy nothing. When he threatened him with demotion and public disgrace the die was cast.

Jacobsz, suffering from a monumental hangover, stamped from the great cabin choked and purple with fury at Pelsaert's lecture. He sought out Jeronimus Cornelisz at once.

A short time after this had happened the skipper went above to Jeronimus and said, "By God! if those other ships were not lying close I would treat that Miserly Dog so that he could not come out of his cabin for a fortnight . . . and were I a bit younger then I would do something else, then we lifted anchor I would very quickly make myself master of the ship." Whereupon Jeronimus asked softly, "Pray what would that be, IF you were younger?" But he would not give an answer for the time being. . . .

Those hot words started the maggot of thought crawling in the evil brain of Cornelisz that was to carry them all—Pelsaert, Jacobsz, and Jeronimus himself—headlong to disaster.

Cornelisz was a strange, deadly creature. He had been an apothecary in the city of Haarlem, a man of pills and potions and education, and he had joined the honorable Dutch East India Company as an undermerchant for reasons best known to himself. Perhaps it was because he found Haarlem too uncomfortable while investigations were going on into the activities of the notorious painter Torrentius and his disciples.

Torrentius van der Beecks was a famous Dutch pianter who, having amassed fame, wealth and fortune with exquisite still lifes, in middle age disgusted soberer citizens by establishing a cult which mocked religion and virtue. He conducted naked orgies of gross obscenity—

which he painted on canvas—and dispensed a twisted philosophy which claimed that nothing, however apparently evil, could be bad because everything came from God and He was Goodness. This was interpreted by his followers as meaning that they had license to practice any immorality they liked, and they did, with enthusiasm and to the scandal of all Haarlem, before respectability mustered forces and marched against them.

In 1627 Torrentius was arrested and, after leading his judges a merry dance with his slippery intelligence, indicted. He still had influential friends and was allowed to escape to England, but the magistrates of Haarlem continued a witch hunt after his disciples. Cornelisz had scampered out of Haarlem, but he decided to go farther. A trip to the Indies was an excellent idea, he decided; Amsterdam might not be far enough. When he left Amsterdam he took with him Torrentius' crabbed ideas of good and evil.

While Cornelisz was at the very root of the mutiny plot, Pelsaert and most of the others aboard were deceived by his obsequious manner into thinking of him as a competent and respectable officer. He was clever, persuasive, ingratiating, a direct contrast to the rough-and-tumble skipper. Jeronimus was thirty years old. By report a dandy who loved fine clothes to an almost feminine degree, he knew French and Latin and loved to watch death, though he never soiled his own hands with killing, being a physical coward. His most significant traits were an engaging charm (which deceived even Pelsaert) and a hypnotic hold over the minds of his followers. Pelsaert later wrote bitterly of their alliance:

> Jeronimus Cornelisz, having made himself a great friend and highly familiar with the skipper Ariaen Jacobsz, moulded their similar intelligence and feelings into one; the skipper being innate with prideful conceit and ambition so that he could not endure the authority of any over him. Moreover he was mocking and contemptuous of all people in-so-far-as it did not concern sea-faring . . . But Jeronimus on the contrary was well-spoken and usually knew how to give the polish of Truth to his lying words; he was far more sly and skilled at getting-on with people.

Old salts always claimed that it was unlucky to have women aboard because they stirred up the devil in a man. Predikant Gysbert Bastiaensz, a preacher on the *Batavia,* wrote later: "There arose some trouble between the Skipper and the Commandeur and it was caused by two women, one of whom was mishandled on the ship. Therefore many troubles, *veel moeilijkheden,* have befallen this vessel . . ." The two women were Lucretia van der Mylen and her maidservant, Zwaantie Hendrix.

Lucretia was the young and extremely attractive wife of a junior merchant named Boudewyn van der Mylen, who had preceded her to the Indies. Zwaantie had sailed as her hired maidservant, but antagonism quickly arose between the two. Lucretia was ill-advised in selecting an earthy and voluptuous young woman as her servant on a voyage during which they would necessarily be confined nine months in close quarters with a shipload of women-starved men. And Zwaantie was not her only problem.

Months later Pelsaert was to write in partial explanation:

The skipper had also taken a great hatred to a woman named Lucretia whom he had tried to seduce for a long time and had not succeeded, and therefore he was very embittered towards her. And had chosen her servant Zwaantie Hendrix with whom to spend his time and do his will, who readily accepted the caresses of the skipper with great willingness and refused him nothing, whatsoever he desired; through which the love on both sides became so intense that without taking any thought of his honour or the reputation of his office he had sworn that if anyone made so much as a sour face at Zwaantie he would not leave it unrevenged. At last when they were away from the Cape of Good Hope he took from her the name and yoke of servant and promised her that she should see the destruction of her Mistress and others, and that he would make her a Great Lady.

When the first outward manifestation of what was to come—the assault and outrage on Lucretia on May 14—occurred, Pelsaert recorded with indignation that it "was taken very violently and to the highest degree by [myself] and though still very ill, had thoroughly investigated who had been the culprits."

Every minute now brought Jan Evertsz closer to the roll of execution drums outside Batavia Castle—and many others to worse fates.

The ship surged onward, decks deserted except for the steersman and night watch. Clouds flitted across the moon, throwing glittering patches of brightness upon the sea ahead. Two hours to dawn and another day. . . .

Ariaen Jacobsz, a tall, hawk-nosed figure muffled in a cloak and sheathed in seaboots, strolled stiffly to the lee rail, coughed and spit into the foam below. Then he jerked sharply. Jesu! What was that ahead? Cupping his hands he roared to a man standing for'ard, hunched with cold and silhouetted against the stars like a human crow.

The figure peered uncertainly. A cloud covered the moon and passed on, leaving a fresh square of added brilliance on the sea.

"It's only the moonshine, Skipper!" came the half-apologetic cry.

Jacobsz nodded, satisfied.

Hell, he was jumping at shadows. That conniving Cornelisz. . . ! Their calculations plainly showed the Southland was still a good 600 miles away. No need even to post the masthead lookouts yet. Never mind; in a couple of hours it would be daylight and he'd be able to turn into a warm bunk where Zwaantie already lay muskily asleep. . . .

CRASH!

He was thrown violently against the lee rail. BUMP. . . . RUMBLE . . . RUMBLE . . . GRIND. . . . In a series of drunken lurches and staggers, punctuated by the awful noise of rending timbers and the tearing of the rudder bolts, the ship trembled to a halt and canted hard over on her port side in a mist of spray.

There was a moment of horrible stillness and silence. Then he heard the surf breaking all around them.

Jacobsz' eyes started from his head like a madman. "We're aground . . . wrecked!" he screamed. "That was surf, not moonlight—God's Death!"

Before he could gather his wits Pelsaert was on deck.

June 4th; on the 2nd day of Whitsuntide. I was lying in my bunk feeling ill when felt suddenly with a terrible rough motion the bumping of the ship's rudder. And immediately after that I felt the ship held up in her course against the rocks so that I fell out of my bunk. Whereupon I ran up and discovered that we lay right in the middle of thick spray.

The eyes of the two men met in mutual hate and accusation as passengers, sailors, and soldiers in various stages of undress tumbled on deck in terror. The booming of the surf in the darkness around them sounded the death knell of their ship.

"God have mercy on our souls!"

The wind whipped the cry away into the night.

4 SHIPWRECK

Daylight came.

". . . Thank God, islands!" said Pelsaert, straining his eyes in the dawn. "At least we are not on a rock in the middle of the sea."

They could see two islands immediately ahead of them; miserable islands, so low that at first they thought they were shoals exposed at low tide. The smudge of a larger island showed some miles to the north. But at least it was dry earth where the goods and people could be landed if the ship should break up, and just for the sight of it a number of people led by the predikant fell on their knees and thanked Providence.

In the 4 A.M. blackness just after the ship struck, Pelsaert and the skipper had a bitter exchange. Pelsaert accused Jacobsz of incompetent navigation and not keeping a proper lookout. "I said to him, 'Skipper, what have you done that through your reckless carelessness you have run this noose around our necks?' "

Jacobsz snarled back that he had seen the white of the surf, but the gunner Hans of the night watch had assured him that it was nothing more than the shine of the moon on the water.

"What counsel now?" asked Pelsaert tersely.

The skipper mumbled that God alone knew where they were. He believed himself that they were on a shallow some distance from the Unknown Land (Southland) . . . he thought they were just on the tail of it. If they were lucky and had grounded at low water, a rising tide might float them and they could winch the ship off by pulling on cables attached to stern anchors and winding with the capstan. It had been done often enough before.

"I asked him how deep it was there. He answered that he did not know. I ordered the lead to be fetched, which was in the cabin of the steersman, and I found that astern there was only 17 or 18 ft. of water, but at the forepart of the ship still less."

They began to lighten ship, running the heavy cannon overboard with rumblings and splashes, the gunners almost weeping when they came to jettison the beautiful bronze pieces, pride of their lives, that they had polished lovingly all the way from Amsterdam. "All . . . everything!" cried High Boatswain Jan Evertsz, swinging a rope's end. And so the bronze guns went.

It made no difference. The ship still bumped and jarred with every wave, canted over on her port side so that they "Could not stand or walk," and every strake of timber and cord of rigging creaked and groaned in protest. The yawl was swung over the side to take more soundings and reported seven fathoms of water a pistol shot (100 yards) astern, but practically no water forward.

"We have come on at the high tide," said Jacobsz, his face drawn at the realization of what that meant. And indeed, as the tide dropped, "It began to surf and foam around the ship." The poor *Batavia* began to batter her keel so alarmingly hard on the reef it became obvious that she must soon spring her timbers or drive her mainmast through her bottom like a pike through a herring box.

They resolved to cut the mainmast to save the ship's bottom and because, freed of its great weight of timber, canvas, and rigging, they might yet float the ship. Ariaen Jacobsz himself swung the first blow with the axe into the quivering, outraged timbers. To cut a mainmast was such a serious matter a skipper had to take the first stroke to show his responsibility.

CRASH! The mast fell in such a confusion of canvas, cordage and splintering timber the wreckage completely enveloped the midships section of the ship. A groan went up, and Ariaen Jacobsz cursed silently and bitterly, while Pelsaert made a gesture of despair. The mast had fallen not overboard but athwartships, so that the vessel still carried its weight. It grossly hindered the ship's boats in the lee, and a broken section of topmast began to thump like a battering ram on the ship's side.

The sun came up, showing them the brilliant blues and greens of the coral water around them, and whitening the gray banks of the islands. But the beauty had no appeal to the frightened people on the *Batavia's* canted deck. They could see death in the spuming surf, death in the dry land beyond, white and brittle as human bones. The gulls would pick their bones on these God-forgotten banks at the end of the world —they were sure of it.

The passengers milled around the deck, some still in nightshirts, demanding to know what had happened and where they were. The voices were shrill and hysterical. Looking for someone to blame for their fear, they pointed at the skipper. It was his fault—he had done this terrible thing to them. Blame him. . . .

"Quiet, you cattle!" roared Jacobsz.

"Let my sailors work. Ships have been on banks before and got off. With God's help we'll get off this one."

But it was not to be.

"God the Lord chastised us with many rods," wrote Pelsaert sorrowfully.

By 8 A.M. they had virtually given up hope of saving the ship.

Therefore I sent the skipper to two small islands or rocks not far from the ship, to see if the people and some of the goods could be saved there. About the ninth hour he returned . . . Reported that the islands would not be flooded so far as he could see. Because of the great Clamour of Women, Children, Sick, and Poor-hearted men we decided to put most of the people on land first and meanwhile to get ready on deck the money and the most precious goods for which I did my utmost.

There were brutish scenes as the passengers struggled for seats in the boats going ashore. Men pushed and fought, trampling over women and children in their panic to leave the ship. There were screams, shouts, oaths and wails; mothers were separated from children, husbands from wives. Sailors roared and cursed above the din, trying to limit the people in the boats to a safe number, fending desperately to prevent the frail craft from being smashed against the ship's side by the surge, and at the same time trying to load barrels of bread and water which might yet save all their lives on these desolate and uncompromising desert islands. Every time the boats came alongside the nightmare was repeated.

Worse things were happening below. The soldiers and gunners were looting and had broken open the wine and brandy barrels. They rioted drunkenly about the ship, interfering with the efforts of the seamen to bring up bread and water from below decks. "Our goodwill and diligence were impeded by the Godless unruly troops of soldiers as well as crew and their women whom I could not keep out of the hold on account of the liquor . . ."

A macabre carnival below. Wolf-pack panic on deck. A ship smashing herself to pieces on a reef near unknown islands in an unknown sea —God knew how many miles from anywhere . . . God the Lord chastised us . . .

At 10 A.M. there was a great shriek below decks. The ship had burst. The tough oak, agonized after hours of pounding on the sharp edges of the reef, had parted at last. Thousands of gallons of green seawater flushed through the holds and lower cabins of the ship. It was impossible to know whether any cowering souls had been trapped. In the face of the general emergency individuals had ceased to count. What was really catastrophic was that the sea had flooded the fresh water barrels and swamped the bread locker. Some of them would die for want of that water.

So the day wore on. The crippled ship shuddered in her agony like a dying, beautiful broken bird. The thunder of the surf, remorseless, triumphant, battered the *Batavia* without respite, thumping and smashing along her sides, rolling over her, around her, past her, breaking with a noise like a roll of execution drums.

All on board was bedlam: drunken shrieks and laughter from the hold; querulous, whining, white-lipped fear from the gutless passengers on deck. In the midst of the confusion the mouths of a few honest sailors compressed with contempt for their shipmates, as they labored to save the precious food and water which might keep some of them alive long enough to reach Batavia in a ship's boat. Batavia—a city 1500 miles away across treacherous and unknown seas. . . . Already they were thinking that it must soon be every man for himself. The closeness of death made life suddenly very precious. Each man had only his own life to lose—or save. Honor, ethics, other men's opinions, what did they matter now? Life. Life. Life. It had never been so dear. The message rumbling in the surf was very clear.

The sailors knew that there was a chance—a slim chance—of some of them navigating the largest of the ship's boats to Java. It would hold only about 40 men, of the 316 in the ship's company, and they must take as much water and food as they could carry, regardless of how little they left behind. If the boat did not reach Java the people on the islands must die. They would probably die anyway before the Company could send a rescue ship south, judging by the tiny amount of food and water they had been able to save. Bad luck for them. But if it came to a choice of whether they all died together or the seamen saved themselves—why then, there could be only one decision. The behavior of the soldiers aboard and the passengers ashore made them feel considerably less guilty about their intentions, which for obvious reasons they kept to themselves.

The soldiers had grossly hindered the attempts to salvage food and water on the ship. The passengers were behaving like idiots and worse ashore.

About sunset the skipper came aboard with the yawl which had taken to land a Casket of Jewels and some people, said to me "It won't help at all that we save water and bread, for everyone on land drinks as much as he can. To forbid this has no result unless you order it." By this time we had put on land 180 souls, 20 casks of bread, and some small barrels of water.

Pelsaert claimed later: "That day all the people, if they had so desired, had been very well able to get ashore. But some had their eye on drunken drinking, others went on plundering . . ." So he went ashore with the skipper at Jacobsz' request to restore order, intending to return with the next boat to fetch the money chests from the sloping deck. But Pelsaert never set foot on the deck of his flagship again, and the chests—all but one—went to the bottom of the sea. That one was smashed open by the French soldier Jan Thirou with an adze in the wine-stupid plundering which followed Pelsaert's departure from the ship. "And so the whole chest was for the most part emptied, and at last, in drunkenness, had thrown the money at each others' heads."

On the wreck that night the mutineers—those who were not comatose from a surfeit of ill-gotten grog—gathered in the great cabin. Jeronimus was wearing one of the Commandeur's splendid red-lined cloaks, leaning back in his great carved chair. At his elbow was a bottle of the best Spanish wine, and around him was gathered an assortment of men ranging from the beardless but bloodthirsty cadets to soldiers and sailors in various stages of drunkenness. Occasionally a great wave thundered against the hull and hissed along the length of the stricken ship; but now she was flooded and resting on the bottom.

She was moving very little and the situation was less alarming. Most of the men still aboard were too drunk to care in any case. They were laughing with childish delight at being in the Commandeur's quarters, and the cabin was filled with intoxicated clatter. Allert Jansz had broken into the Commandeur's desk and chest and emptied out all his personal belongings. Letters, medallions, family pictures and company seals clattered to the floor and were trod on.

Pelsaert's journal was discovered, and opened and read aloud by Cornelisz, the text interrupted by many ribald remarks as he riffled through the pages making random selections. Raucous laughter greeted the passage dealing with the outrage on Lucretia van der Mylen. But soon they tired of the amusement and the journal was ceremoniously fouled and flung overboard to the waves.* It was followed by an assortment of other items from the Commandeur's chest and luggage—some valuable, some purely Pelsaert's private property, and an object of petty spiting on that account. Among them was a gold medallion with the image of Prince Frederik Henry of Holland belonging to Pelsaert. The oafish young sailor Cornelis Jansz put it in his hat with other looted items and threw it all into the sea, shouting, "There goes the rubbish, even if it be worth so many thousand guilders!"

Cornelisz, who watched the looting with an indulgent and only fractionally superior smile, had at first hoped with landsman's naïveté that the embarkation had been premature and that there was still a chance to repair the ship and float her off. With the money and cargo aboard they might still have a rich prize. Jacobsz had dashed his hopes, curtly asking him if he were mad or drunk that he couldn't see that the ship was finished. She had less chance of floating than a hearth brick. Her back was broken, he said, avoiding Cornelisz' eyes, and with the great ballast and cargo weighing her down to the bottom she would stay there till she broke up. He brushed the undermerchant aside and jumped down into the sloop.

Cornelisz watched him go with a narrowed gaze. Could it be that Jacobsz regarded himself and the other mutineers as an embarrassment now that the plan had miscarried . . . ? Would he be pleased to see the sea overwhelm the wreck and drown them all? A dangerous thought. He looked around and regained confidence. The wreck

* This was the journal Pelsaert kept from Holland to the wreck reef. Subsequent journals kept after the wreck survived.

seemed solid enough. Ariaen Jacobsz would come back—if only for the money still in the chests stacked on deck.

Cornelisz expressed his confidence to his fellow-conspirators in the great cabin that evening. They dined fatly on food from Pelsaert's larder brought in by the capering cabin steward Jan Pelgrom, and drank fully of fine wines and raw, throat-stinging gin. A taste of days to come, Cornelisz assured them. The drunken roaring of the soldiers still drinking in the hold sounded faintly through the thick oaken doors.

On a little island, huddled over an inadequate fire of green sticks for warmth, Francisco Pelsaert saw the pin-point of light in the great cabin on the wreck. And wondered. . . .

Jacobsz, sleepless under his cloak on the island shore by the drawn-up boat, already had his plan clear in his mind. Jeronimus Cornelisz had made a grave error of judgment concerning his hold over the Skipper.

5 DESOLATION AND DESERTION

Forty-eight hours after the wreck the desertions began. Pelsaert and Jacobsz were in the first boat, which slipped away before dawn on June 6. They sailed from a little cay, later to be called *Verraders' Eylandt* . . . Traitor's Island . . . with bitterness by those left behind. In the sloop were Pelsaert, gray at the enormity of what he was doing; Jacobsz, brooding over the loss of his ship, but confident of navigating the little sloop to Java; Jan Evertsz, awaiting an opportunity to slip a knife into the Commandeur's jugular; Zwaantie Hendrix flouncing her skirts; and a tight-lipped crew of seamen.

The second boat, the yawl, with Uppersteersman Claes Gerritsz, Understeersman Gillies Fransz, and eight remaining sailors, followed only twenty-four hours later, sailing to catch up and to complete the abandonment of the people on the islands and the wreck. Forty-seven people, including two women and a three-month-old baby, saved their lives in the boats in this way.

Behind them they left 250 people "Being in the utmost misery, and likely to perish shortly from thirst and hunger," with far less food and water than they had taken in the boat for a much smaller number. The 70 men on the wreck were left to swim ashore or drown, the 180 people on the island had water only for one or at most two days. The Company's chests of silver were left on the disintegrating deck of the wreck to go to the bottom of the sea.

Quite suddenly water became more precious than silver, and nothing more precious than life itself. It was the law of survival, the instinct which has made cannibals of men in open boats. The black-backed rock crabs clicking among the stones, the sharp-beaked seabirds fluttering overhead . . . they would have understood. This was the condition of their world: Death to the weak. But Pelsaert and Jacobsz, senior civilized officers? Was it really as Pelsaert later claimed—that he and the others had ". . . Decided and resolved to do our utmost duty in order to help our poor companions in dire distress. In token of the truth has signed with our own hand and have sworn . . . this 8th. of June, 1629."? Or was it as basic as the Crab of fear and thirst pinching his parched gullet, the fear he saw in the eyes around him, the thought of death, with human rib bones lying about like cages on the white coral slabs of these miserable islands so far from God and fatherland? The sailors with him could see no hope for the others—no hope for themselves if they delayed even a day.

Whatever his reasons, Pelsaert *did* leave. On the day following the shipwreck, June 5, he sailed to the wreck from the islands as he had promised, intending to take off the treasure and the men remaining aboard. But wind and sea had risen so much that the sloop could not make seaway sailing—she needed leeboards—and it took Pelsaert from morning until noon in the yawl to reach the vicinity by rowing. He said he could not approach the stricken vessel.

Waves broke even over the poop . . . I remained a long time in the vicinity of the ship to wait for an opportunity for me to get aboard. But in vain. At last there was a carpenter, Jan Egbertsz of Amsterdam, who was bold enough to swim to the yawl through the surf, whom the Merchant Jeronimus Cornelisz with at least another 79 men who were on the ship had sent with a request to help them for there was for them no longer any safe place on the ship.

But he could not help them. "How great a grief it was to me all reasonable people can imagine," he wrote. Pelsaert sent Egbertsz back with the gloomy suggestion that they build rafts, and asked them to throw some planks overboard to make leeboards for the boat so that they could take off the treasure.

The weather worsened as the day progressed and the situation of the men on the ship became more critical. "In the afternoon it started to blow very hard out of the North West and the ship was pounded very much that day by the waves, so that one could hardly see it and it was a miracle that it remained together." The sailors were not concerned about the men aboard. Now they wanted only to save themselves. As seamen they were realists. They knew how tough it would be on the long voyage, how precious every drop of water. Even a day's delay . . .

> That evening [the day after the wreck] we calculated our water which we had in the small barrels and we found ourselves on the smallest island where we were with the boat and the sloop with less than 20 gallons of water where we were with about 40 people, and on the largest island where there were 180 souls, was still less . . .

The seamen demanded to take the sloop which could carry thirty men or more (the yawl was smaller, carrying ten to search the big islands. If no water was there they must go to the mainland, and at least one of the boats must go to Batavia without delay to fetch a rescue ship. Otherwise, as Pelsaert said, "We should perish all together. Which was what the Skipper told me, saying otherwise the seamen would take the boat."

Pelsaert made a token protest.

> I proposed that we should see the outcome of the weather and the ship. For to leave such a large group of fine people and the goods of the Company aboard, I would be responsible before God and my High Authorities in Batavia.

The sailors "promised, that on whatever land we should find water, be it on the islands, or the Southland they were willing to turn back and assist the other people with as many water trips as were found to be necessary . . ." But they were adamant that they must leave at once. Pelsaert did not take much persuading. The truth of what they said was obvious.

> At last, after having discussed it very well we weighed-up that there was no hope of getting water out of the ship unless she should break up and water barrels come ashore, or a good rain should fall—and these both very uncertain—we resolved to go searching. If we could find none we should sail with God's Grace to Batavia to relate our sad, unheard-of, disastrous happening.

He did not say why it was necessary for him to go with the boat.

They slunk away in the dark, though Pelsaert claimed he made an attempt to tell the islanders of his intentions. He told the sailors he must row over and inform them, rather than leave without telling them: "Better and more honest to die with them . . . than to stay alive with deep grief of heart," he penned in his journal. But he did not tell the people.

At first Jacobsz would not provide a crew to row him over in the yawl "They will keep you there and you will regret it," he said. Finally when he got a crew and neared the island, the sailors panicked when the people came running down to the water's edge. "They will keep you and us, Sir!"—and they would not go any closer. He wrote that his desire to tell them was still so strong, Jan Evertsz had to pull him down in the boat to stop him from jumping over—a statement which has been read with cynicism by some historians. But it may well have been that the sailors wanted to take unhappy Pelsaert with them as their authority for leaving—they might otherwise be accused of desertion. And of course Evertsz had his own plans for the Commandeur.

Pelsaert finally wrote their intentions on a piece of paper and left the message tucked under a bread barrel on their little island to be found after they had slipped away before dawn the next day. He said that they were going to the other islands and if necessary the main Southland to look for water, and he promised they would return as soon as possible. It was three months before they would see him again. The embittered survivors named the cay Traitor's Island in memory.

The seamen *did* land on the big High Islands (Wallabi Islands) five miles north of the wreck and spend a day searching and digging fruitless holes in beaches. But in their general fear and distrust of each other they probably did not search very hard, or too far from the all-important boat. They missed the water that could have supplied enough for all their needs. Next day they built the sides of the boat up higher with planks for the rough seas ahead. The fact that they had thirty-six people aboard, including two women and a baby, and were heavily overloaded seems to prove that in fact their real intentions were to sail to Batavia. With the yawl in tow they sailed from East Wallabi Island, the silhouette of the wreck and the island with the deserted people still visible in the distance, and steered for the brown bulk of the Southland and the scent of gum leaves below the eastern horizon.

Back on the island the people were already short of water. Lack of discipline had lowered the barrels dangerously. Soon they were scraping the slimy bottoms of the casks with their pannikins. And then there was none. They began to pray and die. Some drank sea water and went mad, others drank their own urine. They cursed the names of Francisco Pelsaert and Ariaen Jacobsz with their dying breaths. Men drowned trying to get ashore from the disintegrating wreck.

On June 10, six days after the wreck and four days after Pelsaert and the ship's officers had left them, a miracle occurred. Rain fell.

"It was too late for some," Predikant (Pastor) Bastiaensz wrote; but for the survivors it was a joyous reprieve. They let it run down their faces, danced feebly for joy on the wet coral flagstones, and when their thirst and jubilation were sufficiently quenched, they rigged the sails from which the tents were made to catch the drenching rain in barrels.

"God is merciful! He has not forgotten us," cried the Predikant.

They were to doubt that in later weeks. Leaderless and believing themselves abandoned, the wretched folk on the islands were easy prey for Jeronimus Cornelisz.

6 DEATH MAKES A PLAN

Jeronimus Cornelisz was the last man to leave the ship. This was no grandiose gesture. He simply could not swim and after watching others go bubbling down to drown in the breakers, he would not trust himself to wash ashore clinging to a barrel or spar. For eight days he stayed on the wreck while great spray-smoking seas broke over the remains of the poor *Batavia* and huge sections daily splintered away under the battering, until it virtually fell apart around him.

On June 12 he was washed into the beach clinging to the bowsprit spar. Forty other men had drowned swimming from the wreck, but he was saved. The people were overjoyed. "God be praised, the under-merchant!" they cried when they found him weak, speechless and floundering in the shallows. "We thought you were drowned, Sir!"

It was some time before Cornelisz was himself again; but when he regained a little strength, warm in borrowed clothes, with good food in his belly, he found that things were very much better than when Pelsaert had sailed away. Rain had filled the water barrels. Many casks of food, wine and water had washed up from the ruptured wreck, and a constant watch was kept for new kegs and barrels drifting past in the current. The mainmast had washed in, bringing enough sails to provide tents for everyone. Rafts on which some of the soldiers had floated from the ship were a means of getting from island to island. Carpenters were building flat-bottomed boats from wreck timbers.

The critical day after Pelsaert's departure on the 6th had been June 10, when they had been without water for more than twenty-four hours and the weakest of them were dying every hour with parched throats and blackened tongues. But that evening the storm filled their barrels and saved their lives.

There was plenty of natural food on the islands and in the waters around them, now that they had the strength to look for it. There were birds' eggs by the bucketful; the birds, having no trees in which to nest, burrowed like rabbits in the ground and could be caught when they fluttered home at night. Big friendly seals flopped on the beaches, lethargic in the sunshine. Having never seen men before they sensed no danger and were easily run down and killed. They made a roast for a score of hungry men. Fish flickered through the coral shallows, taking baited lines greedily. "Though of different taste and form than on other coasts," they were still delicious eating, and a few hours in the channel with a heavy line produced enough flapping jewfish, snapper and barramundi to feed the whole camp.

In short there was no reason—provided they caught rain whenever it fell, and husbanded their water thriftily—why they could not all have lived there many weeks in good health and spirits.

No reason?

Cornelisz was aghast when he found how the mutiny plot had progressed in his absence. David Zeevanck, the bull-shouldered young clerk, and Coenraat van Huyssen, the handsome aristocratic cadet, took him aside at the first opportunity and whispered urgently. The secret of the shipboard conspiracy was out.

Ryckert Woutersz, a gunner, had drunk himself into a sorry state of inebriation when he learned of the skipper's departure and had blabbed the plot to everyone, declaring himself abandoned by the skipper and asking in drink-slurred and lugubrious self-pity whether this was fair reward for a man who had been prepared to risk the gallows on Jacobsz' behalf. He got his reward—a dagger between the ribs in the darkness—but not before the damage had been done. Tho whole camp had buzzed with rumors, especially when Ryckert's disappearance was noted the next morning.

Cornelisz bit his lip in vexation. The flap-mouthed tool.

"Now we want to kill the others," said van Huyssen flatly and without emotion. "We are tired of rations. The water may not last forever, and it is foolish to feed so many useless mouths."

"*Ja,* we would keep a few women though," said Zeevanck, looking toward Lucretia van der Mylen's tent.

Cornelisz intercepted the look and frowned. "Leave it with me," he said at length. "We must be circumspect in this matter. If we frighten them, there are enough able-bodied soldiers and men-not-of-our-mind on this island to defeat us twice over. We must walk softly. I will devise a strategy. In the meantime you will do nothing that will arouse suspicion. Understand? Nothing."

He kept them fidgeting twenty days before the first murders. "This merchant in the beginning behaved himself very well," Predikant Bastiaensz wrote sorrowfully at a later date.

The matter was skillfully planned. It was not easy. Jeronimus had a nucleus of only about twenty men in his immediate circle of conspirators. Against them were more than 150 people. At first sight the odds would seem hopeless; but among the conspirators were most of the senior and educated men, the assistants or clerks of the Company, and the junior officers (cadets), many of whom came from aristocratic families and treated the common people with an air of authority which they accepted. Cornelisz himself was senior V.O.C. man on the spot once Pelsaert and Jacobsz had left, and as undermerchant he took charge of the people on the islands by the rightful authority of the Company. Everything was done in the name of the Company by its appointed servants. Ironically any protest or move against the mutineers would itself be termed "mutiny."

Cornelisz had the poor common folk bluffed and bewildered until it was too late for them to do anything but pray, and when it came to that stage they found no mercy in the cold eyes of his killers. Cornelisz had skillfully harnessed their subconscious hatreds and the result was an outburst of savagery which was to horrify the Dutch-speaking world —in an age when death from many causes was so common people were not easily upset by it.

In Batavia much later, Antonie van Diemen wrote:

A horror to all Christian ears. The Undermerchant Jeronimus Cornelisz of Haarlem, following the beliefs of Torrentius with some of his accomplices in wicked intent—by rumour having become aware that the previous evil mutiny was known and should a ship be sent for them, on arrival at Batavia they would not escape the burden of their misdeeds—have come to more evil things. Having the intention to kill all except about 40 people with whom they thought they had a chance to run off with the yacht that would be sent for them, and so seek their fortune. In which horrible and horrible intention they proceeded. . . .

That was the plan: Seize the rescue ship. But first they had to become masters of the islands.

Cornelisz' major problem was to get rid of a group of soldiers who had so far proved disconcertingly loyal to the Company and quite outrageously incorruptible. It was a disappointment to him that out of the considerable number of soldiers whose muscle and fighting skill would have been most useful to the mutineers' cause, only a few had been won over. Among these were Mattys Beer, Andries Jonas, Wouter Looes, and Lance Corporal Jacop Pietersz, called "Stone-cutter" or "Window-frame," who hated the world for his twisted face and awkward body, and was hated in return. But the ones who caused Cornelisz concern were older men, veteran mercenary troops with the scars of many campaigns. Some were English, some Flemish, a number of them French. They lived apart from the rest of the passengers, sailors and V.O.C. men, aloof and slightly scornful. Their orderly tents, neat little fires, and weapons stacked pyramid-fashion beside them contrasted sharply with the amateur muddle of the civilians. These men were professionals, used to tents and rough fare—and to fighting.

Cornelisz had no conscience, and would have had no qualms about killing them on the spot. But they were dangerous men. He knew that they could whip his following of cadets, malcontent Company men and unblooded soldiers with contemptuous ease, if it came to physical conflict. How then to be rid of them? Especially Weibbe Hayes.

Hayes was the epitome of the Dutch East India Company soldier: seasoned, tough, courageous, with cast-iron loyalties. He had been too honest beneath his buff leather jerkin for the sly advances of the mutineers aboard the ship. There had been no mistaking his angry reaction. Cornelisz knew that he and the others must be put out of the way. But how?

The return of one of his island-built boats from an unsuccessful exploration of the High Islands to the north gave Cornelisz his idea. The crew told him that the land was alternately sandy and rocky. There were vast mud flats difficult to cross, and from their observation the islands were at least as barren as their own. There was no water.

"Tell no one these things," Cornelisz commanded. "Tell them instead that there is much water, many birds and eggs. We will send the soldiers on a false errand." Weibbe Hayes and his men could march their legs off looking for the water which didn't exist. And when they failed to find it—why then, they could die of thirst.

The soldiers were sent without their weapons, Cornelisz explaining that they would need all their strength to carry water barrels. Twenty-two or more were dropped off on the islands. They were to send up smoke signals to attract attention when they found water, and they would be picked up by the boat, Cornelisz told them smoothly.

"Like hell we'll pick them up," grinned Zeevanck as they rowed away from the beach.

The next step was to divide the remaining company among three islands—their own Batavia's Graveyard, the little cay of Traitor's Island and the long island across the channel called Seal's Island because they hunted the seals on its far beaches. Cornelisz explained it away by saying that this was necessary because Batavia's Graveyard was overcrowded. It would be better from the point of view of hygiene, hunting and gathering firewood if the company were dispersed a little. Contact would be kept through the boats and rafts. It was the Commandeur's will. . . .

If the good people had perceived that their lives were at stake they would certainly have made a stand. But the conspirators prevented such a thing because they chose 20 to 24 of the most willing Muyters, whom they divided with their weapons into two tents, taking away all weapons from others who had any. . .

The stage was set. The young noblemen cadets were secretly practising swordplay and craving to be killing. A brittle atmosphere took hold of Batavia's Graveyard. Cornelisz dismissed the elected Council and replaced it with one of his own choosing . . . Davidt Zeevanck, Coenraat van Huyssen, Lance Corporal Jacop Pietersz.

The sands were running out for honest men. Folk started at shadows and rolled their eyes fearfully at noises in the night.

"It is time," said Cornelisz. "Kill the strongest first, and at night. Tell the other folk they have gone to the High Islands."

The cadets would have their blood. Cornelisz' own prize would be the shrinking white body—very beautifully alive—of Lucretia van der Mylen.

And so the murders began.

7 BLOOD ON CORAL SAND

Pelsaert and Jacobsz arrived at Batavia on July 7, three days after the first murders on the island.

"God be praised and thanked," wrote the Commandeur.

It had been a hard voyage. More than 2000 miles on the course they had steered in an open, overcrowded boat, short of food and water, battered by the sea, blistered by the sun, frozen to the bone at night. They had nearly perished in a storm before the journey was properly underway, on June 10, the night rain fell in the islands. A shrieking northwest gale caught them on a lee shore near where Port Gregory is now marked on the map of the West Australian coast. They had to cut the yawl away from tow and let the waves take it, throwing overboard everything that could be spared, even bread, to lighten the craft, desperately bailing and rowing during the dark hours of the night until the storm abated.

Finding it impossible to land because of the heavy surf, they forged northward, awed by the huge waves and towering red cliffs until finally they were able to make a landing on Australia near 23 degrees (about 300 miles north of the wreck) and drink some water from miserable rock holes where aborigines had drunk some little time before.

In his journal, Pelsaert wrote:

There lay bones of crabs and ashes of fires. It appeared that it had not rained for a very long time, nor was there any sign of running water, for beyond the heights the country was flat again, without trees, foliage, or grass, except for high anthills thrown up of earth . . . was also such a host of flies which came to sit in the mouth and eyes that they could not be beaten off. . . .

This miserable land was probably somewhere in the vicinity of Point Cloates. They scooped about twenty gallons of water from the rock holes, sighted some black men who ran away, and sailed on northward. Evertsz desperately maneuvered his position in the boat to try for that one moment of general inattention when he might stab Pelsaert and tip him overboard. The chance did not come.

They were out of sight of land for eleven days in rough and squally weather before they sighted the purple mass of Java late in the afternoon of June 27, anchoring prudently offshore for the night. In the morning, "We found a waterfall. Thanks and praise to God, we could quench our great thirst at last; here we filled our casks and before noon were again under sail"—west along the Java coast toward Batavia. Evertsz still waited.

At sunset on July 2, they saw a sail astern and dropped an anchor to wait for it. It was the yacht *Sardam,* one of the fleet over which *Batavia* had been flagship, and with her, consort ships now appearing over the horizon.

Pelsaert's feelings can be imagined. He had left Amsterdam in the finest vessel of all as Fleet President. Now here they were in rags, emaciated skeletons, unshaven, stinking in filthy clothes, hollow-cheeked as skulls from their privations, and their beautiful ship smashed on a reef many miles south. And the people . . . who could tell what had happened to the people?

Pelsaert went aboard the *Sardam* choked with emotion and from her to the big merchantman *Frederick Hendrick,* which had caught up with the rest of the fleet, though she had left Holland three months later. Heer Rameborch, a Councillor of India, was aboard her.

Therefore I sailed immediately to him where I told his Hon. with heart's grief of our sad disaster. He showed me much friendship and permitted that I should stay on the ship with him until we reached Batavia.

Evertsz had missed his chance.

Governor-General Jan Pieterszoon Coen sent for Pelsaert immediately after he landed. Before the cold, accusing eyes of the most ruthless Dutch administrator of the century Pelsaert found himself stumbling and faltering in his story. Coen's hand slowly tapped the carved arm of his chair as he listened. There was no humanity in his face. Where men or money were concerned he was never merciful, just practical. His tremendous energy and ambitions were completely bound up in the great Company for which he had established a trade empire without parallel in his century. Woe betide any luckless servant of that Company who crossed the aims or interests of the corporate body; his wages, possessions, even his life could be forfeit. No wonder Pelsaert trembled and sweated under the gimlet gaze.

At the end of the interview Coen sent orders for the arrest of Jan Evertsz, the high boatswain. He commanded limp, drained Pelsaert to prepare a written document of evidence against the Skipper Ariaen Jacobsz, and instructed him to attend a Council meeting on Monday morning, July 9—they had arrived on a Saturday. Batavia vibrated with rumors on Sunday. Old friends were superficially pleasant to Pelsaert, but he felt that people had already placed him as a man apart. Not yet found guilty, not proved innocent, he waited in a limbo of justice, a man to be treated politely, but with discretion.

At the Monday Council meeting he was left in no doubt that his action in leaving the people would be examined more fully at a future date. Judgment suspended. Meantime, it was recognized—as he had pleaded—that the most important thing was for a ship to sail at once for the wreck, to save as many people as still remained alive, and salvage what remained of the Company's goods and treasure. They gave him the chance to save something of his reputation. He was given charge of the *Sardam,* with Jacob Jacobsz (no relation to Ariaen) as skipper, and the *Batavia's* Uppersteersman Claes Gerritsz and Understeersman Jacob Jansz to navigate the way back to the island. Among the crew of twenty-six aboard the little *Sardam*—a fast-sailing, clean-lined craft of the class called by the Dutch a "yacht"—were four Indian divers from Gujarat and two Dutch divers who hoped to salvage the treasure chests.

The *Sardam* would sail as soon as she could be unloaded, and revictualed—at the end of the week. Coen's final sailing orders to Pelsaert contained an ominous note: "You shall therefore set sail tomorrow in the name of God and shall hasten your journey with all possible diligence in order to arrive most speedily at the place where you have lost the ship and left the people . . ."

Lost the ship and left the people . . . That was the shadow under which Pelsaert sailed, yellow-faced and fever-gaunt after the privations of the open-boat voyage. The *Sardam* cleared Batavia port on Sunday, July 15, 1629, and sailed for the great Southland.

Against his disgrace Pelsaert had two satisfactions. A fresh corpse swinging on the gruesome gibbet outside Castle Batavia was that of Jan Evertsz the high boatswain, convicted of the charges of the shipboard assault against Lucretia van der Mylen (Her husband, Pelsaert learned, had died while she was voyaging to join him). And Friday the 13th had proved an unlucky day for Ariaen Jacobsz. The Council, with Coen as chairman, had decided: "Because Ariaen Jacobsz, Skipper of the wrecked ship Batavia is notorious through allowing himself to be blown away through pure neglect; and because also through his doings a gross evil and public assault has taken place on the same ship, on the widow of the late Boudewyn van der Mylen, in his life Undermerchant, it has been decided by His Hon. [Coen] and the Council to arrest the mentioned Skipper and bring him to trial here in order that he may answer those accusations made to his detriment."

Evertsz had talked long, loud and clear under torture before they hanged him—but not one word of the mutiny. Hanging was bad enough; they would have broken him on the wheel if they'd thought him a mutineer.

Back on the windswept, gray islands so many days' sail to the south, the course of events was now implacably resolved. Cornelisz was committed to murder; once begun there was no turning back.

On the day Pelsaert sailed aboard the *Sardam,* Cornelisz had his men row across to Seal's Island and murder most of the forty folk he had sent there. They had already killed the people on Traitor's Island, and most of those on Batavia's Graveyard. The plan had proceeded almost too easily. There was only one discordant note in Cornelisz' trump of triumph; a fact as unpalatable as a ship's cockroach in a glass of good *genever* gin.

Weibbe Hayes, whom he had sent to die, had found water.

The three smoke signals announcing the success had ascended into a clear sky on the first day of the general massacres. They had continued impatiently, smudging the horizon for a day or two more, then they had abruptly stopped.

Jeronimus scowled deeply, rightly guessing this to mean that the soldiers had been warned. Despite his care some of the people had escaped in the darkness, swimming with rafts and pieces of timber to the High Island, gasping the horror of the happenings on the islands near the wreck to Hayes and his men, looking fearfully back over their shoulders for pursuit.

Cornelisz stared over at the distant streak of the long High Island for a long time. They would have to be killed; all of them, soldiers and refugees. Fortunately they had no weapons . . . nevertheless it was disquieting. If a rescue ship came unexpectedly they might warn its crew and upset the plan. But meantime the mutineers had to complete their mopping-up of the few stray, frightened folk remaining on the islands near the wreck.

They already had killed most of the people. The strongest were killed secretly at night, ambushed with swords as they stumbled sleepily to relieve themselves, or called quietly from their tents. They were buried as secretly. Others were drowned from rafts, lured aboard to go fishing or "to go to another island," in twos and threes, and shoved overboard to drown by the mutineers, who always took the precaution of outnumbering them two to one. The people on Traitor's Island—Provost Pieter Jansz of Amsterdam, his wife and child; Claudine Patoys and her child; the cooper Class Harmansz of Mangdenburg, his wife and their children; soldiers Wouter Joel, Christoffel Quist, and Nicklass Winckelhaak; and the old sailors Pauwels Barentsz and Bessel Jansz—had made things ridiculously easy. They built their own rafts to sail for the High Island, but were foolishly seen setting out. The mutineers chased them in one of their beach-built scows and caught them. The women and children were tipped shrieking into the water of the 23-fathom channel to drown. Some of the men managed to swim to Batavia's Graveyard, where they staggered through the shallows calling to Jeronimus Cornelisz for help.

"*Vermoord ze!* Kill them!" shouted Cornelisz, his voice high and strained.

The mutineers leaped forward with eager savagery. "Andries Jonas has stuck a pike right through the throat of the sailor Pauwels Barentsz, who had been thrown underfoot by Jan Hendricsz, until he died . . ." Rutger Fredricx ran with a sword and hacked down Bessel Jansz and Claas Harmansz, who had also swum to the island to plead for their lives and the lives of the families. Blood spouted on the coral flagstones of the island.

"They were traitors, deserting the Company," muttered Cornelisz to no one in particular.

On Batavia's Graveyard the trembling occupants of tents invariably heard their death sentences in the words, "We believe that some of the Company's goods are illegally hidden in this tent. We have come to search." The murder of Passchier van den Ende, Jacop Hendrix and a sick cabin boy on July 12 was typical.

> . . . Whereupon Jan Hendricxz together with David Zeevanck and others who were so ordered [by Jeronimus] took a lamp and went into their tent and asked Passchier van den Ende, gunner, if he had any goods hidden there to say so. He answered weepingly "No" and begged to be able to say his prayers. . . But Zeevanck said "Get on with it." Thus Jan Hendricsz threw him to the ground and cut his throat. The other one Jacop Hendrix, carpenter, begged bitterly for his life. Whereupon Zeevanck and the others went to Jeronimus and said that Jacop was a good carpenter and should be spared. But Jeronimus answered "No not at all, he is only a turner and furthermore he is half-lame. He must also go. He might become a babbler now or later." Whereupon they have gone back to the small tent and Jan Hendricsz threw the foresaid Jacop to the ground and Lenert Miachaelsz sat on his body and Jan Hendricsz stabbed 2 knives to pieces on his breast, also 2 knives on his throat. . . . But could not bring him to death, so that at last he cut his throat with a piece of knife; after that did likewise to the boy.

Perhaps the most brutal murder was that of the Predikant's family on July 21.

Jeronimus kept the old man Gysbert Bastiaensz alive to serve his own purposes. His attractive eldest daughter Judith had gone through a form of mock betrothal with one of the "most willing" mutineers, the cadet Coenraat van Huyssen. But he considered the wife, serving maid and remaining six children in the Bastiaensz family an unnecessary burden on the food and water supplies. So he invited poor, vain, pompous old Bastiaensz to dinner, and with him Judith. The old man went eagerly, hungry for the food, pleased at the honor and hoping that it meant a change of heart in the mutineers' scornful treatment of him. He was pathetically jovial. While they ate and drank, Zeevanck, Hendricxsz, Wouter Looes, Andries Jonas and Andries Liebent went to the Predikant's tent. They softly called out the young serving maid, Wybrecht Claes, and stabbed her, watching the life fade from her horror-filled eyes. Then they stormed into the tent under the pretext of looking for the Company's goods, and began flailing about them with adzes (Jeronimus had suggested these would be effective weapons at close quarters in a crowded tent). The lamp was knocked out, but in the darkness they beat in the skulls of poor Vrouwe Bastiaensz and her six children, including an eighteen-year-old son, and the infant Roelant, who ran between the knees of the mutineers and almost escaped before one of them felled him with a back-hand blow and silenced his tiny cries. The bodies were dragged to a grave which had already been dug, and were shallowly and callously buried. Poor Predikant Bastiaensz became almost demented with grief when he returned from his dinner . . .

The mutineers went from cruelty to cruelty. On the first venture to Seal's Island they killed eighteen men and boys, watched to their chagrin four men (one of them wounded) escaping to the High Island with pieces of timber, but spared four women. This uncharacteristic mercy was short-lived.

Andries Jonas has been ordered by Jeronimus to go, together with Davidt Zeevanck and others with the little yawl to Seal's Island to kill there the remaining 4 women and about 15 boys who had not been killed in the previous murder on 15 July. Therefore Zeevanck has asked whether he had a knife; Andries Jonas answered that he had a knife but it was not very sharp. Whereupon Zeevanck handed him his own knife saying "Cut the throats of the women."—— So Andries has gone to Mayken Soers who was pregnant, has taken her by the hand and led her a little to one side and said to her, "Mayken love, you must die," and thrown her underfoot and cut her throat. That being done he saw that Jan Pelgrom was trying to kill Janneken Gist, therefore he went to help . . . and stabbed Janneken to death with his knife. The other two women and the boys were killed by the others, except three boys who had hidden themselves in the bushes.

They gained some recruits through fear. De Vries joined them to save being drowned, and was later murdered by them, as we have seen, after cutting the throats of nearly twenty sick people at Jeronimus's order. Andries Liebent, Salomon Deschamps and the boy Claas Harmansz were others who were forced to kill to save their own lives. Deschamps, a favorite clerk of Pelsaert's, was made to strangle a baby.

By the end of July most of the murdering had been completed and the number of people on the islands nearest the wreck reduced to Cornelisz' satisfaction. There were still occasional murders, but these were from blood lust rather than any real or pretended necessity—such as the chopping off of the head of a boy called Cornelisz Aldersz on August 16 to prove whether a sword was sharp. They told the boy to sit still blindfolded because they were only having a joke with him. Mattys Beer took his head off with one tremendous swishing swipe of the blade, so that it bounced on the ground like a coconut. Jeronimus laughed loud and high; but Jan Pelgrom "wept because he was not allowed the favor."

A pattern of life had been established. The mutineers could easily be distinguished from their servants—wretched men whom they kept in fear of their lives to fish for them, hunt, and wait on them—by their gaudy dress. Cornelisz set the style.

What a Godless life has been lived here! The goods of the Company which they have fished up, such as woollen cloth, gold braid and other wear, were very shamefully misused by making them into clothes embroidered with as much gold passementerie [trimmings] as possible.

Jeronimus personally appropriated all the Commandeur's clothes and uniforms, using them to

. . . give free rein to the utmost to his pride and devilish arrogance on these poor miserable islands. More, by changing daily into different clothes, silk stockings, garters with gold lace . . . Moreover to all his Followers whom he could best trust . . . he gave clothes made from red cloth sewn with two or more hands of gold trimmings. And created a new mode of Cassock believing that such vain and evil pleasure could last for ever!

And this in an age when even gentlemen sometimes wore their clothes for a week without changing them.

Their servants had none of these luxuries. They were in rags and continually and grimly reminded that they were lucky to be alive. Gysbert Bastiaensz, ailing and grieving, wrote:

I ate seal's skins; and I put some salt water into the tot of water I was given, so that it would last a little longer. They forbade me to pray and to preach. Most of the time I sat on the beach reading, and there I plucked some salad or grass that was there, and then I had neither Oil nor Vinegar. For two months I tasted neither Bread nor Rice. I have been so weak that I could not get up; I had to pull up and push off the little boats with which they navigated . . . Every day it was "What shall we do with that man?" Then one would decapitate me, the other poison me, which would have been a sweeter death . . . A third said "Let him live a little longer, we might make use of him . . ."

Sometimes, as a great favor, Cornelisz would allow the mutineers to see the jewels. They would crowd into his tent, eyes wide and shining with greed, while Cornelisz with mocking deliberation turned the key in the casket Pelsaert had sent ashore, and lifted back the lid with a showman's gesture. They never disappointed him. There was always a wet-lipped gasp when they saw the sparkling wonders inside, intended for Indian kings and princes . . . 58,000 guilders' worth! If he was in a really expansive mood, Cornelisz would let them handle the jewels, passing them around and holding them up to the light. There were two pieces that exceeded all the others in beauty and value. One was a great cameo of agate—one of the largest in the world, Pelsaert had once told Cornelisz on the ship. It had been carved for the Roman Emperor Constantine in the fourth century A.D., and showed the emperor riding victorious in a chariot. It was intended for the Indian Emperor Jahangir. Now it was theirs! Cornelisz boasted. The other piece was also agate, a vase of the same Roman period which had been sent by the artist Rubens to the Indies. On it were carved two faces of the goat-legged, lecherous woodland god Pan. The expression on Pan's face was strikingly similar to that of Jeronimus Cornelisz in certain moods—as when he looked at Lucretia, pale but still very desirable.

Lucretia van der Mylen had been kept alive, as had some of the other women, for a purpose. These suffered the humiliation of having to give in to the mutineers' desires any hour of the day or night that their carnal appetites itched them. It was that or death and they had all seen too much death to want to go the way of the other women. The sisters Trynt and Zussie Fredricx, Anneken Gunner, Anneken Hardens and Margaret Louys (the last two later killed) were made available for "common service." Coenraat van Huyssen claimed Judith Bastiaensz as his own. Cornelisz took Lucretia van der Mylen to his tent. And there—such was the conceit of the man—tried to seduce her gently into sexual compliance as though he were a lover. But his trembling caresses, his French and Latin poems, his Spanish wines and sly potions, even the jewels he offered her from the Company casket, had no effect. She turned her face, shut her tear-stained eyes, and refused to have anything to do with a man who had so much blood on his hands and soul. For twelve days she thwarted and frustrated him. So Zeevanck fixed it in the way one would have expected of him.

Jeronimus . . . complained to Davdt Zeevanck that he could not accomplish his ends either with kindness or anger. Zeevanck had answered "And don't you know how to manage that? I'll soon make her do it." He had then gone into the tent and said to Lucretia: "I hear complaints about you." "On what account?" she asked. "Because you do not comply with the Captain's wishes in kindness. Now, however, you will have to make up your mind whether you will go the same way as Wybrecht Claes [stabbed to death] or else you must do that for which we have kept the women." Through this threat Lucretia had to consent that day, and thus Jeronimus had her as his concubine. . . .

When they became bored with drinking, dicing, squabbling and fornicating, the mutineers' eyes turned north to the High Islands. Murder was a thing that they had never grown tired of, and there were soft throats to cut among the folk who had fled, as well as the weaponless soldiers. Besides, the wretched people there might warn a rescue ship.

"Kill them," said Jeronimus again.

8 DESPERATE DEFENDERS

Historical records of the happenings on the High Islands are sketchy; but anyone who has set foot on the three-mile-long, mile-wide bulk of West Wallabi, known to the *Batavia* people as "the island of Weibbe Hayes," can readily fill in the gaps and picture the sequence of events.

Set ashore on the equally large sister island of East Wallabi, the soldiers spread out in their search for water, climbed the fifty-foot hill that is the highest point in the whole Abrolhos archipelago, and were dismayed at the dull, cheerless nature of the island. There was no water. They looked doubtfully at West Wallabi across the quarter-mile of shallows which separates the two islands, and began to wade across, cursing the shells that cut their feet and the slippery mud which caused several of them to fall and rise blasphemous and dripping. Later they were to bless those shallows and that mud.

Though unprepossessing, West Wallabi proved to have far more to offer castaways than the first large (or High) island. They found birds and eggs immediately. Curious little furry creatures they called "cats" bounded through the bushes. These were tammars, a thirty-inch-high wallaby member of the kangaroo family, peculiarly adapted to life on the barren islands. The castaways trapped them or ran them down. On the back beaches were great broods and colonies of seals. And the low tide exposed countless oysters and shellfish on the rocks.

They used the shells of giant whelks and balers[*] to carry water and cook, and built stone shelters against the bite of the incessant southerly winds. Their first water came from brackish pools of stinking rain-water in the low cliffs, but many days later they found wells in the center of the island—limestone cisterns ten feet deep, large enough for a man to climb down into, with fine clear water in the bottom. They were overjoyed. Well-fed, and with more water than they could drink for the first time since the wreck, they lit their smoke-fires of green bushes with buoyant hearts. Here was enough food and water to last the whole company weeks, months, even years, until a rescue ship came.

Then the first refugees staggered ashore, weak with fright and cold, to warn them of the mutiny. At first Weibbe Hayes was incredulous; but new arrivals, horror still in their eyes and faces, confirmed the incomplete reports of the first ashore and added more detail of blood and slaughter on the islands near the wreck. They came on rafts, swimming with pieces of timber, and one man—Aris Jansz, with a sword-gash across his back and a miraculous story of how the mutineers had left him for dead in the shallows—stole one of the mutineers' home-made boats and rowed across. Soon the soldiers knew the whole story of the mutiny plot aboard ship and ashore—and they realized that it must be only a matter of time before Cornelisz' men came for them. The soldiers now cursed Cornelisz' cunning in parting them from their weapons with ferocious eloquence and something of despair. But besides being fortunate in the fact that Cornelisz had set them down in a land of plenty instead of leaving them, as he had imagined, to die, they were equally fortunate in the qualities of one of their number.

Weibbe Hayes, then a common soldier, was to become famous for his leadership and organization of the defense against the mutineers, a hero of stature whose name would be remembered after many generals and admirals of his time were forgotten. His first move was to have his people, who now numbered forty-seven, devise weapons. Predikant Bastiaensz, who joined them later, wrote: "Of the guns and pikes they made one is inclined to say how is it possible that men can invent such things?" They made pikes from fire-hardened barrel hoop iron sharpened and bound to the ends of pieces of shaped driftwood; they

[*] Giant shells, so named because they were handy for baling out small boats. Also called melon shells.

made morning star spiked clubs from heavy hunks of timber from the wrecked *Batavia* which had drifted up, spiking the ends formidably with long nails; and they pieced together other arms from bits of wreck. Hayes gave them a name—*Verdedigers*, or Defenders—and discipline, drilling them with their pikes and makeshift weapons until they were so arm-weary they could hardly lift them from the ground. Always he accentuated the danger of being caught by surprise.

With this most anxiously in mind, he had an elaborate system of sentries constantly watching and selected a defensive position the mutineers would have to approach (across the shallows): some low cliffs about the height of a man. On the beach and by the inland wells he built two small shelter-forts from distinctive flat-stacked stones, with the chinks packed with mud. When these were completed he made his men carry tons of broken coral rock which was piled behind the cliffs at the strategic spot he reasoned the attack must come. "Ammunition," was his terse reply when they questioned him. Their wells were hidden under wide, flat stones so that the mutineers would not find them if they made a protracted stay. Every day the defenses grew stronger and the Defenders more confident.

The first attack came at the end of July. It followed a treacherous letter written to the French soldiers by Cornelisz—still trying to achieve his ends by cunning—inviting them to defect to the mutineers. It was carried by the cadet Daniel Cornelissen, a swaggering, bloodthirsty little brute who was promptly captured and bound by Hayes' men as soon as he set foot on their island. The letter was carried to Hayes, who read it and warned his men to double their alertness. They waited only a few more days when the lookouts came flying down the beach to gasp that two boats were sighted approaching.

The first attack was a minor skirmish, the mutineers being primarily interested in reconaissance. Led by Jacop Pietersz—Jeronimus stayed at home—the mutineers hoped to find the Defenders as helpless and frightened as the folk on Seal's Island had been, in which case they would have cheerfully chased them, cut their throats and made an end to the business. But finding them full of fight, they did not press the engagement, retreating thoughtfully to Batavia's Graveyard to report to Cornelisz. There were no casualties on either side.

Hayes had deliberately avoided showing his defensive positions or his total strength; he knew the main attack would come later. His principal concern was muskets. His own men outnumbered the mutineers, and their strong defensive position more than compensated for the superior sword and pike weapons of the enemy. But muskets and pistols, though slow-firing and inaccurate at any distance, could inflict severe casualties at close quarters. They would be almost defenseless against them—and he was puzzled why they had not been used. He did not know that Jeronimus was jealously husbanding the slender supply of powder and shot for the projected capture of the rescue ship and was loath to waste any of the precious material on mere unarmed soldiers and passengers.

The second attack came within a week and was desperately fought. The mutineers turned out in full strength. Cornelisz, regally dressed in his finest red cloak and a tall black hat with a brave feather in it, had brought Lucretia along to watch the show. She sat white and stone-faced in the boat while the mutineers bragged, confident of victory.

Hayes allowed them to come to close quarters, slipping and slithering on the mud, before giving the command for the Defenders to pelt them from behind their natural cliff walls with the heavy coral boulders piled there in readiness weeks before. The effect was devastating. The howls and curses of the stoned, skinned and stunned mutineers blended with the mocking hoots and joyful shouts of the Defenders. Hayes' men eventually jumped from their walls and drove the wretched attackers knee-deep in water at pike-point back to their boats across the mud flats, their gaudy finery wet and disheveled, and their pride proportionately muddied. Jeronimus hissed in fury and called them gutless eunuchs.

On their way home the mutineers spitefully killed the surgeon-barber Maistre Fransz Jansz on the eastern High Island. . . .

> Lenert Michaelsz has stabbed him right through with a pike, whereupon Hans Jacobsz struck him a blow on the head with a Morning Star, Mattys Beer has split his head with a sword, and Lucas Gillisz has stabbed him with a sword . . . which gruesomeness he could just as well have omitted because the man was already so hacked and stabbed . . .

This savagery satisfied them somewhat, and they began rowing toward Batavia's Graveyard, glowering back from time to time at the High Islands where the Defenders were jubilantly celebrating their victory.

Only Weibbe Hayes looked thoughtful. He wondered how long it would be before the mutineers came back with their muskets. The peace was to last nearly a month—an unnaturally long time.

By the end of August Batavia's Graveyard was a seething cauldron of discontent. Jeronimus' servant, Jan Pelgrom, "Daily on the island ran around like a man possessed calling out 'Come now devils with all the sacraments, where are you? I wish that I now saw a devil. And who wants to be stabbed to death? I can do that very beautifully,' with such gruesome more devilish blasphemies." The problem was that they had run out of victims and were bored with inactivity. Guilt—for they had done horrible things—probably gnawed at even the most hardened of them, making them edgy and irritable. The defeat by Hayes' men (they spent evenings planning unpleasant deaths for Weibbe) rankled hard. Zeevanck was accused for having said there was no water on the High Island, Cornelisz was blamed for having sent the soldiers there, Allert Jansz upbraided for having failed to kill the man who escaped with the skiff. . . . Morale was low; the thieves were falling out.

Cornelisz saw that some gesture was required, something to put the braggadoccio and swagger back into his men and bring them together again. Accordingly he decided on some promotions and fine new oaths of fealty. The first was a repeat of the general oath of allegiance to each other taken on July 12 and 16. Everyone had to sign it and reaffirm that

> . . . So truly as God shall help us, and will take the same on the salvation of our souls to be faithful to each other in everything. Also that we shall do no harm to any of us undersigned, nor make any plan before the one has warned the other, nor shall anyone without the other knowing it, undertake anything, be it by favour or by hatred. But [shall] assist one another in brotherly affection in all matters that may happen . . . thus done on the Island of Batavia's Graveyard.

Next came an oath of loyalty to Jeronimus Cornelisz.

> Without exception we accept as our chief and Captain-General Jeronimus Cornelisz, whom we with one accord and each separately swear so truly as God shall help us, to be faithful and obedient in all that he shall order us and in so far as the contrary happens we shall be the Devil's Own . . . Actum on Bataviae's Kerkhof, August 20, 1629.

The pious wording is intersting; most of the mutineers had already amply qualified as the Devil's Own. But it was their oath, they signed it, and celebrated it. Cornelisz had announced with due pomp that since there was no trade in the islands he had lost his liking for the title Merchant and would henceforth be known to them as "Captain-General." He had appointed Lance Corporal Jacop Pietersz "Lieutenant General," a substantial rise in military rank.

Those who signed were

Coenraat van Huyssen	Councillor (former cadet)
Davidt Zeevanck	Councillor (former assistant, or clerk)
Jacop Pietersz	Councillor (former lance corporal)
Wouter Looes	Soldier
Gysbert van Welderen	Cadet
Gysbert Bastiaensz	Predikant
Reynder Hendricx	Steward
Jan Hendricx	Soldier
Andries Jonas	Soldier
Rutger Fredericxsz	Locksmith
Mattys Beer	Soldier
Hans Frederick	Soldier
Jaques Pilman	Soldier
Lucas Gillisz	Cadet
Andries Liebent	Cadet
Abraham Jansz	Gunner
Hans Hardens	Soldier
Olivier van Welderen	Cadet
Jeurian Jansz	Sailor
Isbrant Isbrantsz	Assistant
Jan Selyns	Cooper
Jan Egbertsz	Carpenter
Cornelis Pietersz of Utrecht	Soldier
Hendrick Jaspersz	Soldier
Jellis Phillipsen	Soldier
Tweis Jansz	Carpenter
Jacop Heylwech	Cadet
Gerrit Hass	Sailor
Claas Harmansz	Youngster
Allert Jansz	Gunner
Rogier Decker	Boy
Gerrit Willemsz	Sailor
Abraham Gerritsz	Boy
Jan Pelgrom	Cabin boy
Lenert Michielsz	Cadet
Salomon Deschamps	Undermerchant

The inclusion of their names on that list was to prove fatal for some.

The women signed their own oath of carnal obedience. Lucretia signed with a feeling of numb despair. Jeronimus had been making increasing demands on her—the colder she lay the more fiercely the fires of his ardor seemed to burn—and she wished she had the courage to drown herself. The mutineers relaxed with wine on their beards, women on their arms, and foul songs on their lips, warm in the tents in their fine red coats and shirts and stockings. There was laughter in their mouths, but unknown horror nagging deep in their souls—fear, not yet admitted, that their time was running out.

The Defenders watched from their lookouts, shivering as the wind whistled through their torn and ragged clothing, without tents or blankets. If they were deprived of some of the physical comforts, God was good to them in other ways, according to Predikant Bastiaensz. They carved clogs from the stumps of the gnarled, wind-twisted trees, ate well, and drank as much water as they liked. "Water sweet as milk," wrote the Predikant. "Time would fail me to relate how miraculously God has blessed the good ones who were together with water, with fowls, with fish, with other beasts, with eggs in basketfulls: There were also some beasts they called Cats with as nice a flavour as I have ever tasted . . ."

Jeronimus of course was hatching another plan. This time he would outwit Hayes by intelligence, he told his mutineers. Muscle was the way of apes and idiots. The mutineers whistled when they heard the extent of the proposal. The new plan would be carried out on the first day of September, Cornelisz told them, and it could not possibly fail.

9 | MIRACLE AGAINST THE MUTINEER MUSKETS

On August 20, when the mutineers took their oath of allegiance to be faithful in everything to each other "So truly as God shall help us," they would have been startled to know that Pelsaert was only a few miles away. He had actually passed their latitude the previous noon. At that time if one of the huge albatrosses or petrels skimming the waves in the *Sardam*'s wake had soared upward a few hundred feet, its sharp eyes might have picked up the islands wreathed in their garland of surf on the eastern horizon. Because of the curvature of the ocean (most of *Sardam*'s seamen devoutly believed that the earth was flat), the lookouts in her crosstrees did not see the islands, and she sailed on south under a wide spread of canvas, dipping her figurehead through the blue swells of the Indian Ocean.

By August 22, *Sardam* had reached 29 degrees 19 minutes south latitude—the approximate last noon bearing taken aboard the *Batavia.* "The steersmen guessed to be now 15 miles from the wreck." A good guess. Translating the Dutch sea miles into present terms (one Dutch mile equal to three modern nautical miles), the *Sardam* would have been about forty-five miles southwest, in the steersman's opinion. The actual distance was about fifty-seven miles. So, trying to duplicate the last course and sea conditions of the *Batavia,* they turned about and sailed as she had done, in a northeasterly direction.

Unfavorable currents threw them off course. For days they frittered about, while Pelsaert paced the decks in increasing impatience. The sea mocked them with strands of weed, white bones of cuttlefish, birds flying overhead and other signs of land. But still they could not find the islands. The Commandeur glared at Skipper Jacob Jacobsz. Jacobsz scowled at Uppersteersman Claes Gerritsz, and Gerritsz stared back fixedly with compressed lips. At last Pelsaert could bear it no longer. It was ridiculous, he stormed, that they should have taken only thirty days to sail to Java dodging along the Southland coast in a tiny sloop, and now in a large, well-found vessel they had sailed more than fifty days and still could not find the islands, the wreck or the people. It was notorious, Jacobsz replied, that the *Batavia* had been lost through bad navigation, and he was not surprised that her officers' bearings taken on the islands should also prove to be at fault. Respectfully he did not add that it was Pelsaert, not he, who had left the people on the islands. The Commandeur went below in a rage. He was to lose his temper more frequently in the days to come.

On September 5 they sighted the breakers of the southern Abrolhos. "It was dead calm and we drifted alongside the reefs so that we heard the surf the whole night long." No one who had been aboard the *Batavia* could listen to that menacing thunder of the surf without feeling a chill. What if a current should carry them onto the rocks? Another Dutch ship, the *Zeewyk,* was to be wrecked at this spot 100 years later; but the *Sardam* escaped and sailed north. Still they could not find the wreck. They sighted breakers almost daily now, but "We always came too high or low," in latitude.

A map of the Abrolhos archipelago shows their problem clearly. With its overlapping lines of fringing reefs and breakers, it was a miracle that the unhappy *Batavia* had got as far into the maze as she did without running her keel into the corals or being pooped by a greybeard roller. And, as Jacob Jacobsz had suggested, Ariaen Jacobsz the skipper and Claes Gerritsz had been incorrect in their shore sighting on the islands. They had said "28 degrees, 15 or 20 minutes," an error—"The which has caused not a little misunderstanding in search of this place, and also loss of time," Pelsaert later wrote crossly in his journal. The wreck was actually on the line of south latitude 28 degrees 30 minutes.

By September 13 they had been sailing sixty days and were becoming desperate. Previously they had stood away from the breakers and foul ground. But now, despite the inauspicious date, they resolved to take a chance.

On 13 ditto, 3 hours after sunrise we again noted white foam of reefs ahead and this place being known to us as the most northerly point of the Abrolhos. Therefore I resolved . . . because it was very perilous to approach from the outside on account of the high seas and dirty ground to keep bearing beneath the extreme shallow. . . .

They would cross the banks and approach the islands from the mainland direction instead of from the open sea.

It was an anxious passage—on bad days huge waves would sometimes rear and break where the *Sardam* passed—and the leadsman was kept busy taking depths. But soon they were through the foul ground and over thirty fathoms of water again. They anchored within sight of the main Southland (the Australian continent) and expected the next day—if Gerritsz' and Ariaen Jacobsz' bearings were anywhere near correct—to sail west and sight the island.

A storm kept them anchored and frustrated another two days. But on the 16th of September—Hosannah! ". . . Towards evening saw the rocks of our wrecked ship *Batavia* and I recognised the High Island." They anchored for the night, Pelsaert sleepless in his bunk. Were they all dead? Were there any survivors? Would they blame him before the world? Or would there just be accusing heaps of bones and eyeless skulls to bear witness against him?

On the islands the same evening the mutineers were ready for the final assault with the muskets. If they succeeded the *Sardam* would be sailing into a trap; if they failed there would be a hangman's noose or worse for every captured mutineer—though neither the mutineers nor the Defenders had any idea that the *Sardam* was in the vicinity.

On September 2, while Pelsaert was only a day's sail away (if his steersman had known the right direction), the Defenders had scored their most notable victory. It was the day of Jeronimus' plan which he had assured his rascals on Batavia's Graveyard "could not fail." The previous day the mutineers had sent the Predikant ashore on Weibbe Hayes' Island with a message of treacherous truce: "With sweet words and beautiful promises to bring them into the net." And then: ". . . Under the cloak of friendship to surprise them by treason at an opportune time." Jeronimus Cornelisz' plan was to offer the ragged and threadbare Defenders, desperately short of clothing and blankets in the chill archipelago winter, cloth and wine in exchange for the little yawl stolen by Aris Jansz from Batavia's Graveyard. This would prevent the Defenders taking to the water to warn a rescue ship. More than that, the negotiations and peace talks would give some of the mutineers a chance to take the French soldiers quietly to one side and offer them 6000 guilders apiece to treasonably turn on Weibbe Hayes and his men at the time of the mutineers' next attack, thus catching and crushing them in the pincers of a claw. The Predikant, who had no knowledge of the plan, carried the soft-worded message of deception ashore, and Hayes cautiously agreed to talk with the mutineers. "Whereupon Jeronimus went back to fetch the cloth, saying joyfully to his people that they now quite certainly had those folk surely in his hands. . . ."

The next morning Jeronimus went back with 5 of the principal murderers, going ashore to the Defenders with the cloth which he handed out there deceiving them with many lies saying he would harm none, that it had only been on account of the water that he had fought against them. That indeed there was no need to distrust him because some had been killed for those had been mutineers and scoundrels who had deserved it. But that he had left most of the people on the Island Bataviae's Kerkhof because he could not transport them in the two yawls. . . .

Hayes watched with narrowed eyes.

Meanwhile Davidt Zeevanck and some of the others who had come with Jeronimus were engaged to buy over some of the stoutest, [secretly] promising them six thousand guilders if they would take their side, also that they should have a share in the jewels, painting as bright as possible the luck lying to their hands.

The luck of the mutineers was running out. Hayes had been expecting some sort of treachery and when his suspicions were confirmed by a signal from the French soldiers, he had his men fling themselves on the mutineer emissaries, rolling them kicking in their gaudy finery in the dust, while they howled "Treachery!" with the honest indignation of rogues caught at their own game.

. . . and started to tie them up, then one of them ["Lieutenant General" Jacop Pietersz] escaped . . . The murderers [who had been standing with their weapons on a small island nearby, watching] seeing that their principal leaders had been captured began to make themselves ready to attack and rescue them. Therefore to make more sure that they would not be hampered by prisoners, [the Defenders] killed four of the principals and kept Jeronimus Cornelisz bound. . . .

Jeronimus, lying in the dust with spittle on his beard, could not believe it. Only a few minutes before he had been his arrogant, patronizing self, strutting in his fine clothes, dispensing gifts and sweet speech to the ragged Defenders, who appeared to be captivated by his charm. Their leader Weibbe Hayes had seemed uncouth and tongue-tied in comparison, and Cornelisz had never felt more at ease, more in command of a situation, more sure of his powers over men's minds. Then suddenly men had flung themselves at him like mastiffs on a bear, dragging him to the ground.

"Treachery!" he shrieked.

"Shut up, murderer!" A hard fist smashed down on his mouth and he tasted the salt sweetness of blood through his bruised lip. A paralyzing fear numbed him like a man who has tumbled unexpectedly into a chasm and impotently feels himself falling, falling, over and over toward the rocks below. The knives glinted. "No, don't kill me!" he cried hoarsely, not recognizing his own voice.

There was no pity in the ring of faces looking down on him; his death was in their eyes. Cornelisz had seen it a score of times on Batavia's Graveyard. It could not be happening to him, the Captain-General! "No, no!"

They did not kill him after all. Hayes' abrupt order was to bind him. But there was no mercy for the others: Cornelisz watched in horror as their bodies jerked and stiffened, blood spreading and staining the sand.

The mutineers' attack was beaten off and they retired leaderless in confusion and consternation to Batavia's Graveyard to discuss the catastrophic thing which had happened to them. With the exception of Lieutenant General Jacop Pietersz, who was remarkable only for his brutality and not at all for leadership or strategy, their entire high command had been wiped out. Jeronimus their leader had been captured, and might already be dead; Davidt Zeevanck, Coenraat van Huyssen, Gysbert van Welderen and the soldier Cornelisz Pietersz were stiff corpses on the Island of Weibbe Hayes, killed in the same way they had put so many others to death. The remaining mutineers elected the soldier Wouter Looes as their new leader, dismissing the protests of Jacop Pietersz, who felt the office was his. They told "Stone-cutter" contemptuously that he had already led three attacks which failed.

Lucretia van der Mylen waited shuddering in her tent for the demands that might be made by the new leader. But though Wouter Looes had been involved in some of the earlier murdering, he had shown signs of repugnance at later killings. And he had spared at least one man's life. Told by Jeronimus to stab the cooper Jan Willemsz Selyns, Wouter Looes, "Coming near him was so confused in his mind and in such an upheaval that he could not do it, and warned the fore-said Cooper immediately that such had been ordered him but that he would plead for him because he [Looes] was a great friend of Jeronimus." Jan Selyns lived to see the rescue ship.

Looes was kind to Lucretia, protecting her from the other roughnecks who would have raped her with pleasure, and later swore "That he will die the Death if he has touched her dishonourably or has seduced her."

She was left alone in the big tent with Cornelisz' finery and her tortured memories, eyes huge and black in her sunken face. She felt she could not face her husband and confess the things that had been done to her—assuming they ever escaped from the weather-bleached open tomb of these God-forgotten islands. It was well that she did not know her husband was already dead.

On September 17, Wouter Looes mustered his now-frightened and desperate rat pack for the final attack. On the day Cornelisz had been captured they had taken two muskets, but their firing mechanism had proved unreliable and they would not go off. This time they had tested them and there would be no mistake. Under Looes' tougher and more determined leadership, the mutineers at last gained the advantage of their superior arms. Bastiaensz, who had (to his great joy) remained with the Defenders, drew up a new peace treaty in the hope of stalling off the attack. "But they tore that in pieces and have come at us and wounded four men with their Muskets, one of whom has died. . . ." There was no more talk of peace or friendship. The mutineers wanted blood, and having tasted a victory they were hungry for more of it. They regrouped in the yawls offshore, preparing the powder and shot for the next assault. Weibbe Hayes prayed for a miracle. If the mutineers had enough powder and shot, they could pick them off like pigeons. It would only be a matter of time. . . .

Then they saw the sail.

A great cry of hysterical joy went up from the beleaguered Defenders. The mutineers turning, read their doom in the approaching ship and felt their hearts turn to lead. Pelsaert could have chosen no more dramatic a moment. Bastiaensz fell on his knees and, joined by many of the Defenders, sent up a quavering prayer of thanksgiving, tears of joy coursing down his stolid cheeks. The mutineers out in their boats blasphemed horribly. Typically it was Hayes who took the first practical action.

"Quick, the boat!" he shouted. "We must warn the ship!"

The mutineers "Were smitten with fear seeing that their chance had passed and their plan was ineffective." Nevertheless they resolved on one last desperate stroke. They had their swords, pikes, and muskets—they would attack the unprepared ship!

As Weibbe Hayes and four men pulled away in the little stolen yawl, the mutineers' oars hit the water together and they began a grim race for the unsuspecting *Sardam*.

10 THE TERRIBLE RETURN

Pelsaert wrote of that terrible day:

Before noon, approaching the island, we saw smoke on a long island 2 miies West of the Wreck, also on another small island close by the Wreck, about which we were all very glad, hoping to find great numbers, or rather all people, alive. Therefore, as soon as the anchor was dropped, I sailed with the boat to the highest island, which was nearest, taking with me a barrel of water, ditto bread, and a keg of wine; coming there, I saw no one, at which we wondered. . . .

He climbed the high hill on East Wallabi Island, the highest hill in the whole Abrolhos—a mere fifty-foot sand hill. Suddenly he saw

. . . a very small yawl with four Men rowing round the Northerly point; one of them, named Weibee Hayes, sprang ashore and ran towards me, calling from afar, "Welcome! but go back aboard immediately, for there is a party of scoundrels on the islands near the wreck, with two yawls who have the intention to seize the Yacht!" [Hayes] Furthermore, told that he was Captain over 47 souls, who had kept themselves so long on one island in order to save their lives, as the scoundrels had murdered more than 125 persons, Men, Women and Children as well, and that 14 days ago he had captured Jeronimus Cornelisz, undermerchant, who had been the chief of the scoundrels.

Pelsaert's mind went through such a turmoil of tumbling thoughts and emotions that his head swam. Cornelisz a mutineer. . . ? Folk murdered. . . ? Fighting on the islands. . . ? He noted that this soldier, whom he barely remembered from the *Batavia* days, still had his uniform, complete though badly frayed and torn, that he had an air of authority about him, and that the others who had come with him appeared to regard him as a leader. But the merchants, assistants, and cadets mutineers and bloodthirsty murderers? It was too much to believe! More likely that the common soldiers lead by this man . . .

There was a shout from one of the men by the boat on the beach. "The mutineers are coming armed!"

They caught the glint of pikes, saw the sun splash on red coats and gold braid. There was something ominous in the purposeful strokes of their oars even at a distance. A decision had to be made.

"Back to the ship!" ordered Pelsaert. There, with their cannon and muskets they could command the situation, find the truth of this incredible and bizarre story, and discover who had been mutineers and how it had come about. "Bring Cornelisz!" he ordered Hayes abruptly before pushing off. Hayes saluted.

It could now be plainly seen that the boat with the men in the red coats was trying to catch up to them. Fear and uncertainty urged Pelsaert's rowers on. Minutes later, they scrambled up the *Sardam's* side, barely waiting to tie their boat up.

"Run out the guns!" cried Pelsaert. "Break out the arms, there has been a mutiny!"

The redcoats ranged alongside, their awkward beach-built scow bristling with men and weapons. Several of them leveled muskets.

Pelsaert called sternly, " 'Wherefore do you come aboard armed?' They answered me that they would reply to that when they were on the ship."

The *Sardam* crew lined the rail with muskets hurriedly brought from the ship's small arms locker. The small deck swivel-cannon swung menacingly to range on the scow. The mutineers saw that their situation was hopeless and their heart deserted them. The bleak muzzles of the cannon trained on them at a range so short they could smell the burning matches of the gunners awaiting orders. They surrendered without a shot being fired.

[Pelsaert] ordered them to throw their weapons into the sea before they came over, which at last they did. When they came over, we immediately took them prisoner, and we forthwith began to examine them, especially a certain Jan Hendricx from Bremen, soldier, who immediately confessed that he had murdered and helped to murder 17 to 20 people, under the order of Jeronimus. [He told of the mutiny plot.] Saying, that the skipper Jan Evertsz, and still more others, had it in mind to seize the ship Batavia before it was wrecked; to kill myself and all people except 120 towards whom they were more favourably inclined, and to throw the dead overboard into the sea and then to go pirating with the ship. Wherefore Jeronimus and all the people who had been on the island had been certain that the skipper would have murdered me on the way to Java, or have thrown me overboard into the sea. So that Jeronimus, having been for a month on the island after the wrecking of the ship, thought that one should either murder all the people to 40 or less, or else help them to some land, so that when the Yacht came, one could seize it, which has been put into action to that purpose. But they could not fulfil their plan because of Weibbe Hayes.

As the story of the horrible things that had happened in his absence unfolded, Pelsaert's face became white and strained. His voice was almost a croak when he asked, "What of Lucretia van der Mylen? Was she killed with the women?"

"No, she was kept as Jeronimus's concubine."

They watched his face to see his reaction, but gained no satisfaction. Behind the mask, however, he raged with fury. Jeronimus Cornelisz!

In his journal he wrote:

Towards evening Weibbe Hayes brought Jeronimus aboard, bound; I looked at him with great sorrow, such a scoundrel, cause of so many disasters and of the shedding of human blood, and he had still had the intention to go on: However, it was not according to the plan of God. . . . I examined him in the presence of the council, and asked him why he allowed the Devil to lead him so far astray from all human feeling to do that which had never been so cruelly perpetrated amongst Christians, without any real hunger or need of thirst, but solely out of bloodthirstiness to attain his wicked ends. He answered, that one should not blame him for what had happened, laying it on Davidt Zeevanck van Huyssen, and others who had been killed, that they had forced and willed him to it; saying that one often had to do a great deal to save oneself; he denied that he ever had the intention to help in the plan to seize the ship Batavia, or of seizing any Yacht that might come. He said that Zeevanck had proposed this, to which he had only consented on account of his own safety without meaning it. For firstly, he believed that they would never be delivered from the islands. Secondly, he had also heard here on land from Ryckert Woutersz that the skipper intended to seize the ship and to throw myself, the Commandeur, overboard, which made him presume that he would never take the boat to Batavia but that they would veer off to Malacca, or if he or the Commandeur had arrived at Batavia, and some Yacht were sent to rescue them, he Jeronimus, would have given us warning.

"In this manner," Pelsaert said, "he tried to talk himself clean, with his glib tongue telling the most palpable lies, making out that nowhere had he had a hand in it."

They chained Cornelisz for the night despite his protests, and planned a raid on the remainder of the mutineers from the second yawl, presumably now skulking back in their scorpion's nest on Batavia's Graveyard.

Before daylight, I and the skipper of the Sardam, Jacob Jacobsz, went with the yawl and the boat to the island of Weibbe Hayes and got 10 soldiers to whom I gave weapons and muskets, and thus we sailed to the island named Batavia's Graveyard, which was near to the Wreck, where the rest of the scoundrels were, in order to capture and secure them. When they saw us coming they lost their courage, and said to each other, "Now our necks are in the noose," thinking that they would be killed immediately; and when I came ashore I had them bound hand and foot and so secured. Afterwards, the first thing I did was to seek for the scattered jewels. These were all found, except a ring and a gold chain.

The ring was recovered later. Perhaps Cornelisz had given it to Lucretia. Pelsaert does not mention his first meeting on the island with Lucretia van der Mylen. His journal was purely official; there was no place in it for private grief or joy. We are left to imagine this for ourselves. Their time alone that day, and the things they said, remain one of the island's sealed secrets.

Later in the day,

Towards evening we went to the wreck, and found that the ship was lying in many pieces, that a piece of the keel, with the flat of the hold, all above water had been washed away except a small piece of the bulwark which was above water. It was almost exactly in the same place where the ship had first struck—a piece of the forecastle of the ship was broken off and thrown half on the shallow, there also were lying 2 Pieces of Cannon, one of brass and one of iron, fallen from the mounts. By the foreship was lying also one side of the poop, broken off at the starboard port of the gunners' room. Then there were several pieces of a less or greater size that had drifted apart to various places, so that there did not look to be much hope of salvaging much of the money or the goods.

But I understood from the steward Reynden Hendricx, which comforted me a little, that on a day one month ago when it was very calm, a thing which hardly ever, or rather rarely happened, he went to the wreck fishing (to which they kept him), and that with a pike he hit some money chests, and hoped that they had not drifted away in this time.

That evening Pelsaert ordered the principal mutineers to be taken to Seal's Island, for reasons of security—everyone's. They built a jail of coral slabs for them. For Cornelisz they built a special cell, similarly constructed, at the very tip of the island of Batavia's Graveyard, a sandspit away from Pelsaert's camp. They built it with care, a dark, dank place with little comfort and no chance of escape for its guest of honor.

On 19 September, in the morning, I sent the skipper to bring ashore those who have been kept imprisoned in the ship in order to inquire how they had conducted their lives; namely, Jeronimus Cornelisz, Undermerchant; Jacop Pietersz from Amsterdam, Lance Corporal here Lieutenant Gen., and had been one of their councillors; Jan Hendricx of Bremen, soldier, one of the principal murderers; Rutger Fredricx of Groeningen, locksmith; Hans Jacobsz Heylweck of Basel, cadet; Lucas Gellissz from the Hague, cadet; Hans Frederick of Bremen, soldier; Jan Willemsz Selyns of Amsterdam, upper cooper; Hendrick Jaspersz of Montfoort, soldier; Hans Hardens from Ditmarssen, soldier; Jaques Pilman of Pres du Verdun, soldier; Gerrit Haas of Zanten, sailor. I have this day in part begun to comprehend from questioning and free confession, what a godless life is that which has been lived here. . . .

The prisoners were brought before the ship's council, with Pelsaert sitting as chairman. Under the strict terms of Dutch law it was apparent that there was sufficient presumption of guilt to apply torture to the wretched mutineers. The most willing confessions were taken first. Then the more reluctant accused were confronted with the evidence given against them by their fellows. If they denied it, or it was suspected that they were not telling the straight truth, torture was ordered. The torture selected was a simple but effective one, widely practiced in the East: the infamous water cure. It had the advantage that none of the special equipment—such as was needed for the more sophisticated rack—was required, and it was singularly effective in loosening tongues. Canvas was tied around the neck of the accused in such a way that it was as though his head were in the bottom of a bucket. Water was poured in until the level rose above his nostrils. To breathe, the unfortunate man had to swallow enough of the water to reduce the level. But as soon as he had managed to gasp a breath, more water was poured, so that he was continually half-drowning or swallowing. If he remained stubborn, eventually he swallowed such gross quantities of water that his stomach would become enormously distended, and he would look like a great bladder. The torture combined the agonies of bursting and suffocation. Each gasping, rattling breath resulted in the inhalation of more water, until the thorax and abdomen swelled like the grotesque body of some huge, obscene insect . . . and still the torturers poured while the nerves shrieked. None of the *Batavia* mutineers reached the extreme stage. Most of them begged for mercy in a short time and were sulkily ready to tell what was required of them. Physical fortitude was not one of their best qualities; besides, they knew they were guilty, and confession was a psychological relief for men already in the shadow of the gallows.

It was a ruthless but efficient system of justice. According to Dutch law, no man could be sentenced to death on charges of conspiracy or treason unless he confessed to it. If there was a reasonable assumption of guilt, it was legal to use torture, but the accused must give a "voluntary confession of his own free will" not less than twenty-four hours after torture, and witnesses had to be confronted with each other after torture, to compare their statements. If they differed, out came the water buckets again.

Pelsaert, as was required of him, kept a meticulous account of the proceedings. Their prime objective was establishing the guilt of Jeronimus Cornelisz—a task more difficult than they had expected. He was tortured five times, continually altering and retracting his statements, accepting and refuting the confessions of his henchmen, making new confessions, only to deny them a day later, until Pelsaert and his council were driven to the limits of exasperation. Finally, "because of his unstable and variable confessions," they called all the people together on the island, the criminals included, and Pelsaert read aloud before them all the examinations and confessions, asking all the people whether they were the truth. He told the prisoners that if they "had lied to him in the least respect they would have to be responsible before the Divine Judgment Chair. . ."

> Have said and called out as One Man that they would die on it, on the Salvation of their Souls not to have lied in the least in the things heretofore confessed. Thus has the Commandeur again asked Jeronimus why he has mocked the council through his intolerable desperation, saying one time that they spoke the truth, another time that they all lied. . . Confesses at last that he did it to lengthen his life, but that he had done enough evil as said.

Like his tutor in evil, Torrentius the painter of Amsterdam, Cornelisz used every dodge and twist to confound his accusers. But unlike his old master he did not have the physical courage to withstand the pain of torture.

The examinations of the prisoners took ten days. At the end of that time the guilt of Jeronimus and seven of his accomplices had been clearly determined according to law. What to do now? Should they take them back to Java aboard the *Sardam* for execution there, or hang them out of hand on the islands? The crew of the *Sardam* numbered only twenty-six. Divers, while examinations proceeded, had recovered a number of the money chests and these, with the jewels already returned, would be a sore temptation aboard the overloaded little ship. "Some, more hardened, are already impregnated with the bad life while others have sipped a little of the poison and they could easily become wholly corrupted by the richness of the salvaged wealth which belongs to our Lord Masters, which we have now fished up." The sailors earned ten guilders a month. The casket of jewels alone was worth 58,000 guilders—altogether too much temptation for men before the mast. "Therefore it would not be without danger for the ship and the goods to set off to sea with so many corrupt and half-corrupted men." So they resolved to hang the mutiny ringleaders, and especially Jeronimus—"scoundrel, cause of so many disasters and shedding of blood"—on the islands as a warning before sailing, and to take the remainder to Batavia Castle to receive their justice there.

The confessions were read publicly out in front of the tents on the island, surf rumbling in the distance over the bones of the wreck. Pelsaert's voice was cold. For the most part the people looked down at the ground, avoiding their neighbors' eyes. Even those who were not guilty felt that some of the evil had fouled them. The mutineers, cowed and sullen, already felt the rope on their necks. The reading took a long time, for the confessions were lengthy and detailed. As he came to each new case Pelsaert cleared his throat and drank from a pitcher of water; then he read on. Finally he came to the sentences.

Pelsaert announced that Jeronimus Cornelisz, in addition to his other crimes, was also to be indicted on a charge of heresy.

Because we found one gruesome sin in the above mentioned Jeronimus, besmirched in every way not only with abominable misdeeds but also with damnable heresy, declaring that there is neither Devil nor Hell, and has tried to imprint that into the people here on the island—moreover that it is still his daily work to bring with his tongue well-intentioned people to a wrong opinion and lead them from the straight path.——Have therefore unanimously resolved and found good, in the best service of the Company and our Hon. Lord Masters, in order that their ship and the valuable goods that have been fished up here, praise be to God, may be safe against further disaster, to sentence the said Jeronimus Cornelisz, with the worst and most willing Murderers. Accordingly we sentence and condemn with this, that firstly *Jeronimus Cornelisz,* of Haarlem, Apothecary, and late Under Merchant of the ship Batavia, on Monday, being the first of October, [shall be taken] to Seal's Island, to a place made ready for it in order to exercise Justice, and there firstly to cut off both his hands, and after shall be punished on the Gallows with the Cord till Death shall follow, with confiscation of all his money, gold, silver, monthly wages, and all claims which here in India he may have against the profits of the Gen. East India Company, our Lord Masters.

Of the others. . .

Jan Hendricxz of Bremen, soldier, aged about 24 years, who according to his confession and examination in full appears to have murdered 17 to 18 people and helped murder them, as well as having the intention to seize the Yacht that came to rescue them. [Also] . . . *Lenart Michielsz van Os,* cadet, aged about 21 years, who according to his freewill confession has murdered 12 people or has helped to murder them, and who has slept with married Women and has used as his concubine Anneken Gunner wife of Jan Carstensz of Tonningen, and Mattys Beer of Munsterbergh, soldier aged about 21 years old, who according to his freewill confession in full, has murdered 9 people or has helped to murder them, also has kept as his concubine Zussie Fredricx, married Woman. [Also] . . . *Allert Jansz* of Assendelft, gunner, aged about 24 years who according to his freewill confession in full, has confessed to being persuaded by Jeronimus Cornelisz to help to seize the ship Batavia, to which he had consented. As well, he has cut the throat of Andries de Bruyn of Haarlem, Boy, also has helped to murder Jan Pinten, Englishman, and that, one night with the others, he had the intention to kill Aris Jansz of Hoorn, Barber, but through the bluntness of his sword, though he gave him a blow on the shoulder, it did not go through it and the above mentioned Aris escaped in the darkness in the water; as well, has committed many wilful deeds during the wrecking of the ship . . .

All to have their right hands cut off and be hanged.

Jan Pelgrom, servant, aged 18 years of Bemel; *Andries Jonas,* soldier, aged about 40, and *Rutger Fredricx,* of Groeningen, locksmith, 23 years. . . .

These three to be hanged.

There was a long silence when the sentences were finished. The condemned men were white and swayed a little. Finally, Pelsaert, his voice now hoarse and barely audible, said that Weibbe Hayes of Winschooten, whose courage and loyalty had saved not only the lives of those on the High Island with him, but probably also those aboard the rescue ship—Commandeur Francisco Pelsaert included—deserved a reward for his services. Accordingly he, Pelsaert, was promoting

Weibbe Hayes to the rank of sergeant with a salary of 18 guilders a month. Also Otto Smitt of Halverstadt and Allert Jans of Elsen, because of their assistance to the aforesaid Weibbe Hayes, would be promoted to corporal at the rate of 15 guilders per month.

Then he declared that the executions would take place in three days.

A chill, drizzling shower of rain blew in from the sea. But it was not the cold which set people shivering.

11 THE GALLOWS TREE

They hanged them on the morning of October 2, 1629, under a gray, leaden sky.

Cornelisz had made several attempts to cheat the rope. First he asked to be baptized, hoping to gain a week or fortnight in which to foment a new mutiny from his cell. They granted permission for baptism but no extension of time. "So that he began to rage, saying 'I see they want my blood and my life. But God will not suffer that I shall die a shameful death. I know for certain, and you will all see it that God will perform unto me this night a miracle so that I shall not be hanged." Fearing suicide the Commandeur ordered the guard that no one should hand him a knife or anything else with which he might damage himself. Despite the precautions Cornelisz took poison.

> . . . it started to work about one o'clock in the morning, so that he was full of pain and seemed like to die. In great anxiety he asked for some Venetian theriac [an antidote to some types of poisons compounded of many drugs]. At last he began to get some relief because apparently the poison had not been strong enough.

Pelsaert noted dryly: "But he had to be got out of his prison certainly 20 times during the night because his so-called miracle was working from below as well as from above."

On Sunday, September 30, with the executions scheduled for the following day, Cornelisz sulked in his prison, refusing to attend a church service. "See how miraculously God the Lord reveals his godlessness before all the people. . . ?" Then he claimed he had a wife in Batavia, and that if the council were humane, they would allow him to live until he had seen her. No one believed him. Finally he launched into a tirade, saying that

. . . there was neither Devil nor Hell; also that he still tried to maintain here in his prison that all he did, whether good or bad God gave the same into his heart . . . For God was perfect in virtue and goodness and so was not able to send into the hearts of men anything that was bad because there was no evil or badness in Himself!

The preachings of Torrentius the painter.

Pelsaert labeled them "gruesome opinions," and forbade people to listen. But there was a macabre and compelling fascination in that condemned voice chanting from the cell. The only way to silence Cornelisz, it seemed, was to hang him as quickly as possible. Then, to cap everything, the weather turned against them. The sea was so rough they could not row the condemned men across to Seal's Island on the appointed date of October 1. Cornelisz crowed and said God had done it. But next day wind and waves had abated, though the sky was gray and lowering, and Pelsaert announced that the executions would take place.

Watched by all the people on the island, the manacled prisoners were led shuffling down the beach on which they had once strutted with swords and scarlet coats, to the waiting boats. Over on Seal's Island the gallows, already built from wreck timbers by the carpenters, stood stark against the sky.

Pelsaert was as pale as any of the prisoners. He was a merchant, not a judge or a hangman, and he did not relish death, judicial or otherwise. On the opposite shore the condemned took the last short walk of their lives, taking short steps in their fetters to the gibbets and chopping block, on the soil where only a few weeks before they had joyfully murdered the boys and women of Seal's Island.

Coming there the condemned begged that Jeronimus should be hanged first so that their eyes could see that the seducer of men died.——But Jeronimus could not reconcile himself to dying or to penitence, neither to pray to God nor to show any face of repentance over his sins. But they all shouted at each other "Revenge" . . . some evil-doers shouted revenge at Jeronimus and Jeronimus shouted at them. At last he challenged them as well as the Council before God's Judgment Seat that he would seek justice there with them because he had not been able to get it here on earth.

So they cut off his hands and hanged him, still screaming "Revenge" as the rope tightened.

Allert Jansz and the others died as hard and unrepentant as they had lived. Jansz, on the ladder with the rope around his neck and a bloody stump where his right hand had been, warned Pelsaert that he had better watch his back on the *Sardam* "Because quite many traitors remained alive who would seize an opportunity to execute that which they had intended." Their last sight in life was the island of Batavia's Graveyard across the water and the white foam of the reef where the ship had been wrecked. Mattys Beer and Andries Jonas tried to gain a few precious minutes of life by dry-mouthed confessions to additional murders, which were meticulously written down before the ladders were pulled from under them and they were jerked out of this world on the rope.

At last they had hanged them all but for the boy Jan Pelgrom. Hysterical with fear, "Weeping and wailing and begging for grace," they left him until last. The boy who had wanted to kill someone in preference to eating and drinking, who had carried the death sentence of half a hundred men from Jeronimus to his assassins, now could not walk, and was quite unable to mount the gallows ladder. In disgust Pelsaert spared him; there had been enough blood and death. Between sobs Pelgrom implored "that one should put him on an island and let him live a little longer. Therefore on account of his youth. . . ." They brought him back in the boat with them to the island—and to the astonishment and considerable annoyance of the folk there.

An uneasy relief settled on Batavia's Graveyard. It was hard to believe that that restless, relentless, evil intelligence was dead. Everything about the island was tainted with memories so strong, they half expected Jeronimus to come walking back out of the dead. His wicked harvest had yet to be reaped in full; there were still a number of mutineers in irons, and many people under suspicion. Pelsaert cautiously decided that with the arch-villain out of the way and the horror of the hangings firmly imprinted on the company, the danger of a resurgent mutiny was now reduced sufficiently to bring the rest safely to Java in chains. "Lieutenant General" Jacop Pietersz could be carried to Batavia life forfeit, to allow the judges there to get their teeth into a major mutineer and make a fine grisly showing of justice outside Batavia Castle—a deterrent to other potential malcontents and thieves in V.O.C. domains. The judges could be relied on to make his death spectacular and unpleasant. Wouter Looes still had to give a full confession—he had resisted torture more stubbornly than the others. Then there was a bevy of minor mutineers and a few unfortunates like Pelsaert's favorite assistant Salomon Deschamps, who had been made to strangle a baby by Jeronimus to save his own life . . .

Persons who have behaved themselves on this island not guiltlessly, but through all too great fear of death have not restrained the murdering scoundrels. Closing their eyes and dissimulating instead of maintaining and setting against the others Justice, their own Honour, God, and Salvation, but on the contrary have smirched their hands with the shedding of human blood, though they have been forced to it.

It was another six weeks—November 15—before *Sardam* cleared the islands with her pathetic bird-cage full of prisoners. The divers raised ten of the twelve chests of silver (leaving one jammed beneath a cannon . . . the other had been broken and scattered during the looting after the wreck), and some gold and silverware. The sailors and soldiers collected fragments of wreckage all over the northern section of the archipelago, picking up even barrel hoops in Pelsaert's desperate energy to redeem himself by leaving nothing of the slightest value behind. In such petty searching the *Sardam* skipper, Jacop Jacobsz, and three men were lost in the *Sardam*'s sloop and drowned during a squall on October 13. Another tragedy.

The prisoners continually implored Pelsaert to sentence them in the islands, believing rightly that he would show them more clemency than the rock-hearted, revengeful judges of Batavia. Reluctantly he did so, dealing out no death sentences, "Using Grace in place of rigour of Justice," but keel-hauling, doses of 100 lashes, dropping from the yard-arm—"These underwritten punishments most nearly accompanied by death. . . ." Salomon Deschamps signed his own sentence (to be keel-hauled three times and flogged with 100 strokes) in contrition. These punishments were to be carried out aboard the ship as she sailed northward, as and if the opportunity occurred. Some mutineers were punished aboard, but most of them were retried in Batavia and lived to curse the day their mothers ever brought them into the world. The two most fortunate were, without question, Wouter Looes and Jan Pelgrom.

Looes and Pelgrom were marooned (as Pelgrom had snivelingly

requested under the gallows) on the Australian mainland. They were given one of the beach-built scows, well-provisioned and watered, and some trading goods, "and may God give them a good outcome in order to know once and for all what happens in this Land." Pelsaert's instructions to them, recorded in his journal, show a pleasant and compassionate side of the man. He advised them to seek out the natives and gave them mirrors, beads and Nuremberg wooden toys to help them make friends.

> Having become known to them, if they will then take you into their Villages to their chief man, have courage to go with them willingly. Man's luck is found in strange places; if God guards you, will not suffer any damage from them, but on the contrary, because they have never seen any white men, they will offer all friendship. Meanwhile, you shall observe with all diligence what material, be it Gold, or Silver, happens there to be found, and what they esteem as valuable. So that, having come to friendship with them, you may be able to ask, by signs and by learning their language, that a lookout should be kept for ships, or for people coming from the side of the Sea, in order to obtain from them more of such goods as iron, Copper, or Nurembergen, of which you have with you several samples which without doubt will please them greatly. The time that the ships make the Southland there, is in April, May, June, July, wherefore you must look out keenly at that time, and seeing any, give suchlike signs as shall appear to be done with purpose, be it with smoke or otherwise. Above all, keep God in mind, never forget Him; and without doubt He will keep you close in His shadow and will yet vouchsafe, at the last, a good outcome. ——Thus done on the Yacht Sardam this 16 November, 1629.

They lowered the scow over the side on a fine, bright sunny morning with the smell of the eucalyptus strong off the Australian coast, just north of a large, friendly river. The fetters were struck off and Looes and Pelgrom, rubbing their wrists, stepped down carefully into the loaded craft. They sat for a long time watching the *Sardam* sail away.

Their story may well be among the most interesting sagas of early Australian history; but we will not know it, for they were never seen or heard of again—though later ships were instructed to keep an eye out for them. They were swallowed up by that huge, mysterious, unknown continent called the Southland. They may have been drowned in a few days or weeks, trying to sail north. It is more probable that they were taken into the tribe by the gentle Murchison natives, and they may have lived for years—two centuries before the first white settlers came to Western Australia—taking aboriginal wives and fathering a clutch of coffee-colored children who wondered why their fathers were always looking hungrily at the sea. So far from the windmills and green fields of Holland . . .

On December 5, the *Sardam's* anchors splashed into the muddy tropical waters of Batavia Roads. At that moment many of the chained mutineers would have cheerfully changed places with Looes and Pelgrom, dead or alive.

12 MORTAL MEN

There were spectacular hangings outside Batavia Castle on January 31, 1630, with drums rolling, bright flags flying from the battlements, soldiers in rows, and the whole town turned out to hiss and screech their vituperation at the wretched men drawn up in the carts. Salomon Deschamps was among the condemned, with a halter around his neck. "Lieutenant General" Jacop Pietersz, a chalk-faced shadow of the beefy, brutal "Stone-cutter" of the Abrolhos after the tortures and imprisonments, was given star billing. He was to be "Broken from under upwards and the body exposed on a wheel," by order of the judges. The others received savage sentences "On account of their abominable gruesome cruelties and suchlike unheard-of murders of men and raping women . . ." As they had nervously anticipated, there was no sympathy for them in Batavia, where righteous indignation and horror at their misdeeds ran high. The executions were ordered by Governor Specx (Governor Jan Pieterzoon Coen had died of a seizure in Pelsaert's absence) and the Council, and there is a later note to say that they had been carried out.

The hangings and broken bodies at sunset that day marked the end of the *Batavia* mutiny. But what of the others: Weibbe Hayes, Ariaen Jacobsz, Zwaantie Hendrix, Predikant Bastiaensz, Lucretia van der Mylen—how did they fare? And particularly Francisco Pelsaert. . . .

The good soldier, Weibbe Hayes, deservedly came home to glory.

Governor and Council made him their favorite. They rescinded Pelsaert's promotion of him to sergeant at 18 guilders a month as inadequate, and gave him an officer's commission with 40 guilders a month. He was a hero, a famous figure in Batavia before vanishing into the mists of history. Ariaen Jacobsz and Zwaantie were still in the dungeons. We have no record of the skipper's end—though the relevant missing papers may one day come to light in some archive. But the outlook for him was black at the last reference. This was in a letter from Councillor Antonie van Diemen to the directors of the Company in Holland, dated June 5, 1631.

Ariaen Jacobsz, skipper of the wrecked ship Batavia, is still imprisoned, although has several times requested a relaxation and a return to the Fatherland. On the strong indictment of having had the intention to run off with the ship Batavia, he has been condemned to more acute examination and has been put to the torture.

His own confession was needed. Hard as nails, Jacobsz had resisted them then nearly two years—enough time in the damp, steaming, fever-ridden dungeons of Castle Batavia to kill most men, even without a sentence. In the same letter van Diemen asked for a directive from the directors on the matter. Did Jacobsz then escape the rigor of the law? It is unlikely. The evidence against him was too strong, the indictments too complete and too many. It is probable that van Diemen was asking the directors to bend the law with this unbending man, to permit him to dispose of him with or without his own confession.

Zwaantie's fate would hinge on Jacobsz'. Preacher Bastiaensz sufficiently recovered from his great grief over the loss of his wife and family to marry again in 1631. He died of dysentery at Banada, India, in 1633. His daughter Judith, concubine of the mutineer Coenraat van Huyssen (killed on Weibbe Hayes' Island), married twice and was widowed twice in successive years after the wreck, and was left destitute. Notice of her plight was brought to the High and Mighty Seventeen and they made the extraordinary generous gesture (for those careful men), of granting her 300 guilders for her widowhood, and a similar amount in recognition of her ordeal, "on the wrecked ship Batavia close to the Southland."

Pelsaert? He paid pennance many times over for that questionable departure from the islands. His health and spirit were broken by the physical ordeal of the small boat voyage and the mental stress of the disastrous state of affairs he found on his return. His last letter to the

High and Mighty Seventeen is almost incoherent—very different from the clear, concise notes earlier in his journal.

He wrote of himself:

> It is our honour that the zeal towards the General Company has been greatly strengthened through continuous grief and sorrow of the heart, which can scarcely be forgotten or ignored by me; and now for the first time I can clearly see and realize that a human being often finds that his worldly welfare has fallen into the hands of 2 or 3 perfidious men. At present, the pack of all disasters has moulded together and fallen on my neck, yea, not quite possible to express with the pen, will moderate same as much as possible, and though I have cried out my eyes, shall be able, by the Grace of God, to resume due service and duty such as I have always endeavoured in service to the Company. . . .

Pelsaert badly needed a rest. But at a time when the Company clerks rose at 5:30 A.M. and worked through until 6 P.M., when even the Governor-General held his first audience at 6 A.M. and the last one at 6 P.M., and did not have a single day's holiday during the year, rest cures were unheard of. The stupefying hours the Dutch worked in the cause of their commercial empire (they had a proverb in Holland: "Jesus Christ is good, but Trade is better") resulted in golden returns for the great Company and acres of gray gravestones marking the last resting places of Company servants. More than eighty percent of clerks going to the Indies died there within three to five years, killed by the climate, gin, sickness, but most of all, unreasonable and unremitting hard work. Among the dead, another victim of the God Guilder, was to be Francisco Pelsaert. His continuous grief of heart lasted only a few months for, by September, 1630, he was dead. His death was obliquely noted in the Council minutes of Friday, September 13. In a later note van Diemen remarks that Francisco Pelsaert "has died in Batavia after a long illness."

Van Diemen was intensely critical of Pelsaert's actions in connection with the unhappy *Batavia*. This may have been partly due to personal rivalry—the two men were about the same age, and van Diemen (a favorite of Jan Pieterzoon Coen) may have resented Pelsaert's meteoric rise; but it is probable that he was also reflecting popular and official opinion in Batavia at the time. There is no doubt that both Governor and Council were cold to Pelsaert after his return from the islands. Though Pelsaert was sent on a trade mission to Sumatra in April of 1630 as Vice Commandeur to India Councillor Pieter Vlack—an important post—the *Batavia* affair was far from forgotten or finished with. Investigations were continuing. In June, van Diemen wrote on behalf of the Council to the Seventeen (directors of the Company) in Holland.

It is certain that a completely Godless and evil life has been conducted on the mentioned ship [Batavia] of which both the skipper and the President Pelsaert are greatly guilty, may the Almighty forgive their sin and make good the damage to the Company; we think it good that Your Honours should look into the proceedings regarding the skipper and give an order in this matter, the accusation is great and the fact that the ship and people have been so shamefully left, through which such a great disaster has arisen, cannot be excused.

A short time later Pelsaert was dead. But even after his death the Company would not relent. They confiscated his due salaries and refused them to his mother in 1632 when she applied for them. Even Hendrik Brouwer, by this time Governor-General at Batavia, failed to move the directors on the matter. Antonie van Diemen later became a famous Governor-General.

How guilty was Pelsaert of any real crime, and how much was he simply the victim of vile circumstances? Our chief evidence is his own journal, quilled in his neat, concise script and still preserved today in the Algemeen Rijksarchief at The Hague. He writes with clarity and descriptive flair, except at one or two important points dealing with the wreck and the departure from the islands, where he becomes emotional, distressed, and a little incoherent. In these passages there is a strong feeling that he is endeavoring to excuse himself at the expense of others (Ariaen Jacobsz in particular), and he makes some important omissions. For instance, in an official note of how the *Batavia's* people "were consumed," Antonie van Diemen recorded that forty men were drowned trying to get ashore from the wreck, presumably after Pelsaert's boats departed the islands. Pelsaert does not mention this damning fact at any point. Nor does he mention that some of the people left on the islands died of thirst. But Predikant Bastiaensz, in a letter to relatives in Holland telling of the sad end of his family—an important document as the only surviving independent eye-witness account of the wreck and mutiny--said, "Having no drink of Wine or Water in four or five days, so that we had to drink our own water [urine] and also many died from thirst . . ." The reasons for these omissions are obvious. Pelsaert wanted to minimize the effect of his departure with the seamen and the boats, and to avoid a manslaughter charge. But elsewhere, in instances where he is not caught between the anvil of his guilt and the hammer of his conscience, he shows the qualities that gained him his rapid promotion with the Company, and reveals himself as a pleasant, humane and rather likeable man.

There is no doubt that Pelsaert cleaned up the mutiny, salvaged the goods from the ship, and tried the mutineers in a most capable and efficient manner. The trial records show that he was a scrupulously fair judge, and his sentences were moderate by the standards of the day. The prisoners he took back to Batavia were much more harshly dealt with. He spared Jan Pelgrom and Wouter Looes. He carried out no more death sentences after the hanging of the notorious seven, though he remarked that the others deserved them. These qualities of mercy, together with his journals and his previous writings in his India report, give us a picture of a sensitive, intelligent, conscientious, but alas for his later reputation, not physically courageous man.

The Dutch believed that the mutiny and massacres on the islands would not have occurred if Pelsaert had remained with the wretched people as commandeur. Of course it is impossible to say what would have happened. But it is hard to excuse Pelsaert his less-than-honorable departure with the seamen. Van Diemen and the others may have conceded that he could have had no actual foreknowledge of the imminent mutiny, but no doubt they pointed out that it was his absence which allowed the lawless elements to take control so easily. For this reason he must bear heavy responsibility for what followed. Pelsaert himself, suffering "sorrow of the heart which can scarcely be forgotten or ignored by me," undoubtedly felt the weight of the murdered men and women on his conscience when he returned.

It is also impossible to say what would have happened if Pelsaert had not died. But the Dutch East India Company were notoriously cold and implacable where failure was concerned, and the *Batavia* affair had cost them a new ship and a great deal of money. In their eyes, Jacobsz the erring navigator and Pelsaert the defaulting commandeur had a great deal to answer for. Later captains (such as Jan Steyns of the *Zeewyk*) who lost their ships through faulty navigation were dealt with harshly indeed. And eventually—we learn through the *Gilt Dragon* * wreck in 1656—a standing order went out to senior officers that in the event of a shipwreck they must on no account leave the

* Dutch name—*Vergulde Draeck.*

ship or their people, but send junior officers for help. The letter written by Van Diemen on behalf of the Council ("the ship and people have been so shamefully left . . .") and these later edicts seem to indicate that Pelsaert would have had to face charges but for his demise. Certainly his career would have been ruined, and he would have lived in the shadow of the *Batavia* disaster for the rest of his days. Perhaps his early death was kinder for coming before the ignominy of a trial and the further disgrace it would have brought.

As disinterested parties, and three centuries after those tragic events, we can judge him less harshly. He was certainly cruelly unfortunate in having skipper Jacobsz and scheming Jeronimus Cornelisz in the *Batavia's* complement, as well as Jan Evertsz, Zwaantie Hendrix and (because of the provocation of her beauty) Lucretia van der Mylen . . . Lucretia probably knew as much of the mysteries in the *Batavia* mutiny as anyone—perhaps more about Pelsaert's actions and his reasons for them. She married again, in Batavia after Pelsaert's death, and was a godmother on a number of occasions in the Indies and in Holland, though there is no record of her having children of her own. She certainly lived to be an old, old lady. It may be that with her died the last living memories of those four dreadful months on the blood-stained island of Batavia's Graveyard.

Only two things did not change with time.

The shining glories fashioned by craftsmen in the time of the Roman Emperors still exist, reminders of the days when they were pinched and rubbed by the coarse fingers of the mutineers on Batavia's Graveyard, held up to the lamplight in a castaway's tent on a desert island to glint for greedy eyes awestruck at the fortune. The cameo of Gaspar Boudaen is now in the Royal Coin Cabinet in The Hague. The Rubens vase has an honored place in the Walters Art Gallery in Baltimore.

And the islands . . . gray and gnarled, home of gull and clicking crab, seal and screeching gull, gale-blasted, weather-whitened, wave-lashed, ageless. . . . Three centuries later, when we came to look for the wreck of the *Batavia,* they were the same as on the day Pelsaert sailed away with his prisoners, to his death and theirs.

PART TWO

13 SHIPS AND CENTURIES

We arrived at the Abrolhos islands toward dusk on July 28, 1963, slipping in through the same channel Pelsaert had used in the *Sardam* so long ago. But while our ships went driving through with high bow waves and undiminished pace, confident in the unfailing beat of their diesel engines, the *Sardam* had edged in slowly under shortened sail, her skipper justly nervous of the lee shore. Once under the darkening bulk of the High Island and past the first line of reefs to port, we swung sou'west into the sunset to bear down on a bare, arid chip of an island two miles away. Four straggling fishermen's huts were silhouetted, so low, they looked as though they were standing on the dark water. The fishermen called it Beacon Island; but to the old Dutch and our exploring party it was indelibly Batavia's Graveyard.

It had taken five years to find the *Batavia* wreck. Five years. . . . Beside the three centuries and more since Pelsaert sailed away they were only a minute in time. In that longer period many things had happened on the islands and in the unseen vastness of the world across the waves and over the oceans since 1629.

One by one the mutineers' bodies had dropped like rotten fruit from the gibbets. As the years passed the sinister execution poles themselves whitened in sun and storm, finally toppled and fell to lie half-buried in the sand drifts of Seal's Island. The islands became again as they had been for thousands, perhaps millions of years before the *Batavia.*

When the year 1700 turned, the only traces remaining of the brief and bloody kingdom of Jeronimus Cornelisz were probably a few bottles, perhaps the corner of a skull protruding through the sand on Batavia's Graveyard, and the bleached bulk of the mainmast on an islet near the wreck. From time to time Dutch sails appeared on the horizon, sheering away in fright when the lookouts spotted the breakers of the dreaded Abrolhos. Some, like the *Batavia,* saw the surf too late and flew like frightened birds into the net of reefs and breakers. One of them was the *Zeewyk,* wrecked in 1727 in the southern islands. Her crew struggled ashore, quarreled, fought, finally built a sloop from the timbers of their wrecked ship. In it eighty of them sailed with justifiable pride at this accomplishment to Batavia, carrying three tons of salvaged treasure—this after nine months eking out an existence in the islands. Behind them they left sixty dead in the islands and fifty or so who had died of scurvy and sickness on the voyage out and been buried at sea.

Lifetimes rolled by. The islands themselves changed scarcely at all: a sandbank altered here and there by storms, a new sea eagle's nest risen on a headland, an old one fallen down. . . . But explosive forces were changing the old world of Europe. Crowns and kingdoms changed hands, royal heads toppled, armies swayed and fought on bloody battlefields from the Pyrenees to the Russian steppes. The Revolutionary forces of France marched across Europe. Napoleon fired his whiff of grape shot, reigned, and met his Waterloo. The Dutch East India Company, once a powerful kingdom in its own right, became bankrupt and destitute. The British seized the Cape of Good Hope and the reluctant Dutch, with their sea power crumbled, were forced to cede Capetown by a treaty in 1814. Thereafter few high-pooped, white-sailed Indiamen, flying the red-white-and-blue flag of Holland, rolled past the Abrolhos on their way to Castle Batavia and the spice princedoms of the East. Ships still shrieked in the night on the treacherous coral reefs, but they were Yankee whalers, British brigantines, French guano freighters, Australian colonial horse-traders, sandalwooders and pearlers. Many ships sank in the Abrolhos; how many no one knows. The coral covered their bones with quick anonymity.

The first white settlers came to Western Australia in 1829—200 years after Jan Pelgrom and Wouter Looes—to settle at Swan River, 300 miles south of the Abrolhos. The uneasy British wanted to prevent the fickle French (already established in Madagascar, the Seychelles, and India) from gaining a naval base which might give them command of the Indian Ocean. It was not the desirability of the country which attracted them. They found it hot, huge, depressing in its vastness; a dark continent. But they persevered with British doggedness. Civilization slowly followed the settlers and in 1840 the Royal Navy came with theodolite, sextant, and sounding-lead to chart the coast. One of their tasks was mapping the Abrolhos.

Mapping these islands was no easy task in the maze of banks and shallows, but it was no ordinary craft and crew that were assigned to the work. The ship was HMS *Beagle*—the vessel aboard which Charles Darwin as a young naturalist developed his world-shaking theories of evolution. The principal surveyors were Commander John Wickham, Lieutenant Lort Stokes, and Lieutenant Crawford Pascoe, all to become famous men. Darwin himself was not aboard; he had left *Beagle* the year prior to the survey. (A pity because it would have been interesting to have his views on the segregated and adapted wild life of the Abrolhos.) Their map of the islands—which they rather irritatingly insisted on calling "Houtman Rocks" though they had been known as the Abrolhos for more than 200 years (and are still called such by fishermen today)—bears the legend "Pelsaert Group" against the southernmost islands. They gave the specific name "Pelsaert Island" to a ragged spine of thrown-up coral six miles long. The southwest tip of it they labeled "Wreck Point," and the anchorage offshore they called "Batavia Roads." Obviously they were under the impression that the *Batavia* was wrecked at this spot, though in fact she had gone down fifty-four miles away in the northernmost islands of the archipelago. By labeling their map this way, they had everyone nicely fouled-up for 123 years. They had heard the hoary old legend of the *Batavia,* knew she was wrecked in the Abrolhos, and were on the lookout for signs of her. Unfortunately they found wreckage in the wrong place, and were misled into thinking that this must be the site of the famous wreck. They leaped to an erroneous conclusion. Pascoe wrote:

> Finding anchorage for our ship at the south east part of the Southern Islands, near to a narrow strip of sand on the edge of the reef which was scarce large enough to be called an island, we found remains of large timber, evidently a beam of a ship. Though it was an iron bolt of considerable dimensions, but corrosion had gone on steadily so many years that the slightest touch reduced it to the size of a small wire. Near this were found

other fragments which most probably had been part of the same vessel. But the most remarkable item was a copper coin of the Netherlands East India Company, a doit bearing the date 1620 (I think), which was good evidence that these were some of the remains of Commodore Pelsaert in the ship Batavia. So the anchorage which we occupied was named by us Batavia Roads and that particular group Pelsaert's group. . . .

No one knows who were the first people to land on the little island that was really Batavia's Graveyard after Pelsaert sailed away in the *Sardam*. Certainly the mainland Australian aborigines never visited the islands. They had no sea-going craft (frail bark canoes in rivers and billabongs was the extent of their navigation) and did not know that the Abrolhos, thirty miles out and below the rim of the western horizon, even existed. Perhaps it was the men from the three-masted barque *Hadda*, wrecked in 1877 a mile from Batavia's Graveyard under dubious circumstances, who first landed there. Their ship was wrecked many miles off course. They rowed in their longboat to the collection of colonial offices, sheds and shanties at Champion Bay (later to become the important town of Geraldton). There the captain, after telling some untruths about contrary currents and the position of his ship, bought the wreck for £150 at an auction and returned to salvage all the gear from her for his own profit. He could have wrecked her deliberately; such things were not unheard of. During the salvage operation the men lived on the island and perhaps wondered at the quaint old bottles and oddments of brassware and bones that occasionally turned up under their feet. But they were practical men of a sort, not scientific, philosophical or inclined toward history, and so they took no account of what they saw. The last of the *Hadda* crew, a Pilot Gilmore, died in Fremantle in 1933 (the year of my birth). I would have given my eye teeth to have been able to talk to him and find out what the *Hadda* men saw there before generations of fishermen tramped over the islands. For it is certain that there would at that time have been many relics of the *Batavia* still to see. *Zeewyk* relics were to turn up by the dozen as more people went to the islands, and when the men of HMS *Beagle* landed there during their map-making of the 1840's, they saw extraordinary sights.

Crawford Pascoe wrote:

On another island on the west side of the group were relics of a more recent date, among which was another doit [Dutch East India Company coin], which was dated 1700, which we concluded marked the position of the loss of the Zeewyk . . . On this island we found a large number of small glass bottles about the size and form of Dutch cheeses very orderly arranged upon the ground; a few very large glass bottles of the same form; some large brass buckles which had been gilded and some of the gilt still remained; numerous small clay pipes which served to solace our crew with the help of tobacco as doubtless they had done long ago for former owners; and one brass gun of about 3 lb. calibre [about 5 to 6 ft. long] with an iron swivel. The iron however was diminished by corrosion to nearly nothing; it had a movable chamber for loading it which was fitted for a square hole on the upper part of the gun near the breech. But what was most remarkable about it was that the vermillion paint was still on the muzzle. The island on which this was found we called Gun Island. . . .

It is frustrating to think that similar relics may well have marked the site of Batavia's Graveyard and been trodden underfoot and dissipated in the rubbish dumps of seamen and fishermen. The men of HMS *Beagle* took their gun back to London when their mapping was done, along with their charts, records, natural history and geological specimens. It now rests in the British Museum, a link with a dramatic epic in early Australian history.

The 1880's saw the beginning of the modern era, when the first guano leases were taken out by an enterprising pastoral family called Broadhurst. Guano—bird droppings accumulated over the centuries, rich with fish phosphorous—then formed the basis for the best agricultural fertilizer. It fetched high prices shoveled up into bags and sold to farmers to add muscle to their wheat and barley crops. The Abrolhos air was heavy with seabirds whose healthy digestion had proved itself in large deposits of guano on certain of the southern islands where the limestone formation provided a natural platform to hold it. The Broadhursts had gangs of Chinese coolies working and filling little trucks on portable railway lines. Sailing schooners came to take it away. The spades clinked as the coolies, wth straw hats and pigtails, scooped every crack and cranny clean with Oriental thoroughness. They left the islands they tackled bare as billiard balls; only the ruins of their broken stone huts still remain.

It was inevitable that some remains of the early Dutchmen should come to light under their diligent shovels. Guano-rich Gun Island, where the *Zeewyk* men had camped, was especially fruitful. Under the earnest attentions of the coolies the guano deposits melted away faster than the birds could put them back. But before the diggings were worked-out, the nameless Chinese had made an important contribution to history. They turned up such an assortment of sailor's skulls, bottles, tobacco boxes with Dutch inscriptions, beads and trinkets, their boss, F.C. Broadhurst, became intrigued. He believed that the relics came from the *Batavia.* Able to discover only the sketchiest facts in history books, he wrote to Holland. There they were able to find for him an ancient book called *Ongeluckige Voyagie van't Schip Batavia* (*The Unfortunate Voyage of the Ship Batavia*), a 17th century best seller which had horrified all Holland, and which had been compiled from Pelsaert's own journals and other scraps of information by one Jan Jansz of Amsterdam in 1647. Broadhurst was fortunate in being able to find a scholar in Old Dutch in Western Australia, William Siebenhaar, who produced a most competent translation of Janz's journal. It told the whole grisly story of the *Batavia* in greater detail (including lengthy excerpts from the trials) than any of them had hoped for, and the Broadhursts and their circle of friends were not unnaturally excited by it. This was history on their own doorstep. They had the account published in full in a colonial newspaper called the *Western Mail* in 1897, and so the modern *Batavia* legend became established. By that time the error initiated by the men of HMS *Beagle* was firmly believed as fact. The *Zeewyk* relics were on proud display in the Perth Public Library—with *Batavia* labels. The Broadhursts and everyone else were convinced that the scene of the famous massacres was indeed the southern group of islands—after all, wasn't it called the Pelsaert Group? Hadn't Crawford Pascoe seen the wreck with his own eyes sixty years before?

The years rolled on to World War I, and on again to World War II; fishing parties and tourists, visiting the islands from the mainland port of Geraldton thirty miles away, made the pilgrimage down to Wreck Point on Pelsaert Island and stared reverently into the coral waters. "She was wrecked just here," they would murmur. The surf spouting on Half Moon Reef told them nothing; but their imaginations ran riot. A whistling blow-hole on one of the islands, moaning on dark nights, even became known as "Pelsaert's Ghost," and few of the old fishermen would go there after sundown. At that time no one had ever considered that the island of Batavia's Graveyard might be one of the outlying sandy cays of the northern group. Everyone knew that the *Batavia* was wrecked in the southern group. But no one could find the wreck.

Searching for Pelsaert's 8000 rix-dollar chest became a favorite occupation among the tourists. Leather-faced professional fishermen eking out a hard living between the wars sometimes sold the visitors age-worn trinkets or coins they had found—but seldom told where they had found them. No one ever found the chest, and this made the *Batavia* a tantalizing and established mystery.

Of course it was the writers who really made the *Batavia* one of the world's most famous wrecks. They wrote both fact (as little as was then known) and fiction, with particular emphasis on the latter. The original story became more and more distorted. Then an authoress named Henrietta Drake-Brockman of Perth did what no one else had done before her and, in 1948, wrote to The Hague for copies of Pelsaert's original journal. She had been a friend of the Broadhursts as a little girl and had caught their enthusiasm for the story. Now she wanted to write a novel—and what better plot than the *Batavia*?

When she'd read the translation of the journal—taken from the Old Dutch by scholar E.D. Drok of Perth—she made some statements about the *Batavia.* These statements brought such a clatter and clamor about her ears from historians and interested people (and everybody seemed to be interested), she was astonished. The *Batavia* had grown to be something of a sacred cow. She said the ship was *not* wrecked in the south, but in the north of the Abrolhos. She made few friends—and some enemies—with this heretical notion; everyone else went on righteously believing that the *Batavia* wreck lay somewhere in the mysterious depths off the south islands of the Abrolhos. Her novel, *The Wicked and the Fair,* was published in 1957. She gave a copy to my father, a personal friend. I promptly annexed it, and became as ensnared by the story as the ship had been by the reef.

But for me it really began some time before that. . . .

14 BEGINNINGS ARE STRANGE THINGS

Beginnings are strange things. The *Batavia* Expedition may have begun with some distant Viking ancestor from whom I inherited blue eyes and a love of the sea. Maybe it stemmed from a day on the beach with my father when I was five years old.

Our regular walk was along a beach bounded by sandhills (castles behind which I imagined pirates lurking) and the hissing, foaming surf. On this particular evening I'd made a foray into the sand hills looking for sharks' eggs which had washed ashore and was panting after my father on the hard, wet sand with the dogs skittering at my heels when suddenly he stopped and pointed.

"Now that's something you don't often see nowadays," he exclaimed, lifting me up to see better.

A full-rigged ship gliding into harbor was silhouetted against the sunset. Her tall masts raked the evening sky and her sails were gold and dark-red . . . the most beautiful thing. It was 1938 and she was one of the last of the grain clippers, the *Pamir,* later to be wrecked in an Atlantic hurricane. I can still see her now if I close my eyes. Afterward I pestered my father until he bought me a book on sailing ships. That book led to another and another until, in time, I had read all the great sea stories. About the time I turned thirteen, another important event occurred: the start of the Underwater Adventure.

My friend Bruce Lawson and I were skinny-legged schoolboys, tow-headed and burnt deep brown by the Australian summer sun, when we caught our first excited glimpse of the world beneath the waves through the doubtful medium of an old Army gas mask with a short hose attached. According to medical tables our diving careers should have ended there and then. But schoolboys are hard to kill and though we had near-squeaks we survived. I can still remember swimming across a limpid reef pool clear as champagne and being amazed to see three quite large fish just beneath me. I put my head up and shouted, "There's fish here—millions of 'em!", and coughed and choked as the end of the hose went underwater. . . .

Boys will be men. I eventually worked on a newspaper and, for a time, reveled in the slippery turf, roaring crowds, bumps, bruises and occasional glory of professional football. But an opponent jumped on my left leg harder than flesh and bone and ligament could stand, and that was the end of that. Taking up swimming seriously again to strengthen the damaged leg, I became so absorbed in the cool green world of the underwater once more I forgot all about football—except to wonder occasionally why it had ever seemed so important. Diving around Rottnest Island, Bruce Lawson and I discovered the weed-girt skeletons of a number of old clipper ships and barques. The relics we found among their ribs fascinated me, and gradually wreck-diving and searching for the old ships in their sea graves became a major hobby. One wreck in particular held my attention, the whale beside which all the others were mere minnows—the *Batavia.* "One day . . ." I promised myself. In 1958 I was armed with research material, packed and ready to go to the Abrolhos, but had to cancel the trip at the last moment. Twice more I was on the point of leaving to search for her, but wanderlust intervened. Hungry for distant adventure I went off to see the rest of the world first. With fins and goggles in my pack, I traveled to Britain, France, Germany, Sicily, Malta, North Africa. It was a gay, carefree existence.

Some of my happiest days were spent with a Cambridge University underwater archaeological expedition in the summer of 1959 under Nick Fleming. We went to Sicily, together with the Cambridge team, to see a Count at Syracuse, an amateur archaeologist whose activities were widely publicized. He said he had located a complete Roman galley buried in the mud and sand of coastal shallows, an archaeological sensation. The press hovered nearby and TV cameras turned as we dived, but in the end the boat turned out to be rather more recent than Roman times—in fact, I found the exhaust pipe.

The Count never forgave me for quipping, "*C'est une discoverie magnifique!* [we all spoke in French of varying quality] . . . we may have the only Roman diesel engine in existence!"

He lacked a sense of humor and we parted on rather bad terms. But our stay in Sicily had been interesting. To be fair to the Count, he did discover one genuine Hellenic wreck with eroded Greek marble intended for temples in Sicily (Syracuse harbor was the scene of a great naval battle between Athenians and Syracusans in 415 B.C.). And we did manage to find one or two real Roman galleys along the coast, now distinguishable only by their amphorae (huge earthenware vases for carrying oil, wine, and grain) and lead anchor stocks. The wood and iron had, of course, vanished centuries before, whatever the Count may have thought about the matter.

North Africa was even more interesting, a vast, red, barren land which was so similar to Australia in parts—down to the eucalyptus trees planted by the Italians—it made me homesick. We mapped the sunken Graeco-Roman city of Apollonia off the coast of Libya, and found some nice things in the depths, including a statue of a small boy which I lugged ashore in triumph. Local museum officials promptly annexed it, as they had every right to, but I was sad to see it go. Later that year I had a brief but eventful career as a movie stunt diver. We were to have done sequences with Yul Brynner and Mitzi Gaynor, but we never reached the filming location in Rhodes. Sailing from England in our forty-five-foot ketch, we were so smashed up by a Bay of Biscay storm we had to be towed 300 miles into a French port by a Breton wine tanker. A fortnight later the boat caught fire and blew up at its moorings, and we lost the contract and all our possessions.

Arriving back in Australia in 1960, I was poorer in pocket than when I'd left, but certainly richer in experience, and confident that with the knowledge acquired in the practical field of Mediterranean diving, I was ready to have a crack at serious searching for the *Batavia*. We needed a clue, a pointer, something. . . . Then, obligingly, Pop Marten found the human skeleton on Beacon Island.

Beacon wasn't marked on official charts, and showed on the HMS *Beagle* map only as the vaguest of blobs, scarcely distinguishable from the squiggles of coral reef surrounding the big islands of the Wallabi Group. It was just another one of scores of drearv, dull Abrolhos

Islands, platforms of coral slate with a few twisted bushes. Seabird roosts. It gained its unofficial name from a beacon—a stack of coral slabs piled eight feet high on the northwestern corner as a marker by one of the old snapper fishermen. It distinguished the island from the others around it and the name followed. When the crayfish boom came after the war, a few fishermen built shacks there because of the anchorage. Bill and Grace Bevilaqua and Pop Marten were among them.

On this important day Pop had decided to bury some rubbish under the clothesline behind Bill Bevilaqua's fishing shack. He stamped firmly on the heft of his shovel with a broad boot. The shovel blade jarred and clanged, and Pop muttered something about "ruddy coral" to himself before he saw that the object was actually a bone. Since the island was half-built of old bird and seal bones, this seemed to him only slightly less remarkable than finding coral, and he turned the bones aside and finished the job. But later, on reflection, he decided that there was something different about the bones. He had read about the *Batavia* mutiny and it struck him that the bones could be human. The more he thought about it the more certain he became, and it provided him with a good yarn. Old Pop loved to spin a story, and he kept the tale alive around the fire on cold winter evenings—so the Bevilaquas told me later.

"I knowed it was a human skeleton as soon as I clapped eyes on it," he would say, tamping his pipe down with a gnarled thumb. "Remains o' some of them poor varmints murdered hundreds of years ago when that Dutch ship was wrecked in these islands, I don't doubt."

"Go on, Pop—you're getting old," they'd rib him. "That ship was wrecked in the southern group. It was a seal you found."

"I know what I knows," Pop would say doggedly, and no one could shake his belief.

It didn't occur to anyone to actually dig and see whether there was a skeleton or not. No use hurting Pop's feelings by turning up a long-defunct seal. And if it were a human skeleton, it would have to be reported to the mainland police, meaning a lot of trouble and nonsense about filling in forms . . . Maybe even a trip to Geraldton in the middle of the fishing season at the behest of bureaucracy. So the Beacon Island fishermen kept Pop's bones to themselves as a spicy little mystery of their own.

Then a holidaymaker from Geraldton named Max Roylance became so intrigued by Pop's storytelling that he went out and turned a shovel under the clothesline, too. To everyone's amazement—Pop's included, I suspect—it really *was* a human skeleton. It gave Grace Bevilaqua quite a turn to think she had been hanging out the wash all this time with a skeleton grinning up under the laundry. The word soon got out among the other fishermen, and Beacon people rather crossly received the news that the police were coming to make formal investigations. Two detectives arrived, collected the bones in a cardboard box, managed to get in some enjoyable hours fishing between carrier boat calls, and departed for the mainland with official statements from all. Pop had a triumphant gleam in his eyes for days afterward, and his story became considerably embellished. The discovery rated a few paragraphs in the press and brought the controversy over the location of the missing wreck to boiling point again. Henrietta Drake-Brockman said that it showed she'd been right all along—the wreck was not in the southern islands, but more than fifty miles away in the northern group. Opposition theorists howled derision. What did a few poor bones prove? they asked. They could be from any shipwrecked seaman's cadaver, an early fisherman, or even a Chinese guano coolie. What rot to suggest they were from the *Batavia,* when everyone knew she was wrecked in the south.

This was our chance. I suggested to my editor that Maurie Hammond and I should go to Beacon Island and resolve the row by discovering the wreck. Maurie was an undersea cameraman of talent and imagination with whom I had been associated in a number of past projects which had produced good stories for the newspapers. These projects had, of course, allowed us to devote more of our time to our other world below the waves. I spent hours scheming. The editor, who was aware of this, frowned. He was a square-built man with thick gray hair who was fond of inhaling gustily on his cigarette.

"The Abrolhos? What do you want to do there?" His fingers tapped the desk.

"Dig on the island to see whether we can find any more relics, and then look around the coral reefs. There should be some obvious spots where the ship might have gone down."

He frowned at a chart, tapping harder than ever. "Don't you think there's rather a lot of reef to look at?"

I answered him boldly, but he was right about the reefs. The chart was festooned with loops and coils representing leagues of reef. I could see his mind balancing the figures and costs of the venture I was proposing against the chances of finding anything, as well as the nuisance of finding other fellows to do our routine work while we were away. Editors have directors, accountants and shareholders to answer to, and he also knew we liked diving and would use any excuse . . .

He stubbed out his cigarette and lit another, looking shrewdly at me through the smoke. Suddenly he butted the cigarette and said "Yes."

I shot out of his office before he could change his mind.

So, in 1960, began our first assault on the submarine coral castles of the Abrolhos, and the search for the *Batavia.*

Before we left I spent an afternoon with Henrietta Drake-Brockman. She was then in her late fifties, tall, with rimless spectacles, and what our grandfathers would have called approvingly "A fine stamp of a woman"—meaning that she had a mind of her own and could be either charming or formidable as it suited her. She had written a number of books, including the *Batavia* novel *The Wicked and the Fair,* and she had compiled a great deal of information about the unlucky ship and its people. At all the disadvantages suffered when dealing with someone who has known you and your family since you were nine years old and in knee britches, I was trapped neatly in the cross fire of her theories from the moment I entered her eighth-story apartment. The apartment, which she shared with her engineer husband, boasted shelves of good books, many tasteful pictures and ornaments, and overlooked the green sward of Perth Esplanade and the shining mile-wide city reach of the Swan River. I had little chance to appreciate any of them.

"Those wretched people make me so annoyed when they talk about the southern group. Of course the *Batavia's* in the Wallabis . . . Where else could it be. . . ? Milk or sugar in your tea?"

I opened my mouth helplessly, but had no chance to reply. There was a tinkle of teacups from the kitchen, and then: "It's all the fault of those silly surveyors Wickham and Stokes in 1840 . . . Jumping to conclusions like that . . . Now here's where it *is,*" she said, reappearing briskly and stabbing her forefinger authoritatively at the Admiralty chart. Her finger indicated the reefs fringing the southern boundaries of the northern islands marked "Wallabis."

The mass of information she had gathered on the wreck was impressive, and her reasoning clear-cut. Her theory was based on two facts. First, that the small kangaroolike wallabies (the frequently-mentioned "cats" which the *Batavia* people caught and ate) existed only in the northern Abrolhos; there were none in the south. Second, that in the southern islands, where the men of HMS *Beagle* presumed the wreck to be, there was water only on small rocky islets, and none on the large islands. Weibbe Hayes was quite explicit that his water "sweet as milk" was found on two large, high islands—and there were wells on the big East and West Wallabi islands in the northern group. It all seemed to add up to the Island of Batavia's Graveyard and other islands of the ancient saga being in the northern Abrolhos. It was a strong theory—but still a theory, and one requiring final proof: the finding of the wreck.

Theories would have been unnecessary if Pelsaert had recorded a true bearing of the site of the wreck in his journal. In his meticulous way he did write down the latitudes his officers gave him; but the figures were grossly inaccurate. Ariaen Jacobsz and Uppersteersman Claes Gerritsz first obtained a wrong bearing when they took sightings from the High Island with an astrolabe before their open-boat voyage to Java. This error caused the *Sardam* to sail fruitlessly in the vicinity of the islands for nearly a month before at last finding the wreck. The second bearings taken by the officers of the *Sardam* were also wrong. Jacobsz and Gerritsz placed the wreck fifteen to twenty miles north of the islands. The *Sardam* men put the wreck at "28 degrees 37 or 40 minutes"—well south, almost in the Easter or central group of islands.

How did these errors come about? In 1629 ship navigation was by Guess and by God. Navigators could tell how far north or south of the equator they were by measuring the angle of the sun at midday, squinting along the rude sights of instruments such as the astrolabe or the backstaff, and getting their north-south distances (latitudes) with reasonable accuracy —within twenty miles. But longitude (distances east and west) had them baffled. Galileo was still perfecting his system of star sightings (which was to be effective only on land and impossible on a tossing ship), and the Englishman John Harrison did not complete the first chronometer, giving absolute longitudinal accuracy for vessels of the King's Navy, until 1759. Until that time mariners could only make a guarded estimate of the distance they had traveled east or west. They sailed on dead reckoning, guessing the number of miles they had sailed each day. One method of doing this was the use of the log, a block of wood with a knotted line attached. The block (log chip) was thrown overboard at a certain time of day. As sand poured through a sandglass a junior officer counted how many knots ran out, and from this estimated how fast the ship would travel in an hour—hence the term "knots" for nautical speed. Following seas, currents, a poorly coiled line, dampness in the sandglass—all contributed to inaccuracy. A good gale could cause catastrophic errors.

In this age of radar, radio direction beams and supersonic aircraft, we may wonder that any of the old ships ever found their way to port. But the truth is that these navigation aids were only taken as an indication, not an accurate "fix." Old sea captains found their way about by ocean bushcraft; they were experts in oceanography. No race of men before or since has been so knowledgeable about wind, tide and weather. They knew what every tiny cloud, every wind-shift heralded. They could tell from sea birds, floating weed and cuttlefish backbones of a likely landfall days before they actually sighted land. And they possessed a mental inventory of every reef, rock, and headland they were likely to come across in their course. Indeed, they became captains by knowing such things. Shipwreck was common, though the majority of ships reached their destinations, as astonishing as it may seem to us. But when it came to taking a bearing at a place unmarked and saying "We are *here* at such-and-such a point of the map," errors were the rule. Ariaen Jacobsz was 600 miles off in his longitude reckonings when the *Batavia* was wrecked, so the bearings recorded by Pelsaert and his officers were of no practical use to either the southern Abrolhos theorists or to Henrietta with her northern notions.

It seemed clear to us, in 1960, that the only way to settle the matter once and for all was to find the wreck by underwater search. We piled our diving and photographic gear in a Land Rover and turned the vehicle's stubby bows north for the seaport of Geraldton, 315 miles away.

Henrietta's last words were: "When you find it you must let me know AT ONCE. Don't you dare tell anyone else first, you naughty boy." She wagged her finger the way she had when I was nine years old and up a mulberry tree.

We reached the Abrolhos aboard a crayfish carrier boat in April of 1960, rolling in through the reefs accompanied by the green stink of hundreds of rotting sheep heads and bullock hocks carried in sacks as bait for the crayfishing boats. The bait bags were in the stern of the boat; we stationed ourselves in the bow.

A fortnight later in complete dejection we accompanied a cargo of live crayfish in sacks aboard the same boat back to the mainland port of Geraldton. Our expedition had been a complete failure. Or so it seemed to us. Days of swimming in wind-whipped salty water until the corals blurred in front of our eyes had shown no sign of the wreck. Digging on Beacon Island had produced two bones which neatly fitted my own wrist-to-elbow measurement and which Pop Marten (delighted to have us as an audience) was positive were identical to those of his now-famous skeleton. We sent them south for identification—secretly. The secret leaked and a rival news bulletin asserted that

"Skin divers are on the verge of solving the 330-year-old mystery of the *Batavia*."

We were furious. Then a telegram arrived from the office like a slosh of cold sea water.

BONES THE WING OF A LARGE SEA BIRD STOP WHAT ARE YOUR MOVEMENTS?

Ouch!

Further digging revealed tons of coral and so many bones that were obviously those of dead seals, at length we became discouraged and ceased digging. By the time we left the islands, faces cracked with sun and salt, we had found the remains of three wrecks—including the 1877 barque *Hadda,* and a guano barge—but no *Batavia.*

We had made some friends among the fishermen, hard-fisted skippers of little boats, and one of them named Kevin McCagh wrote to the office weeks after we had returned to say that another fisherman, Dave Johnson, had found a large anchor in the shallows near where we had been diving. Could it be from the *Batavia*? "That cursed guano barge again," we grumbled, and thought no more about it. We were to remember the anchor and the name three years later; but we had no idea then of how close we had been to the *Batavia.*

Back at the office, my editor eyed me sardonically. Southern group theorists sneered. I growled that it all proved nothing except that there was a hell of a lot of coral underwater in the archipelago. I even fell out in a mild way with Henrietta. She disagreed with us that Beacon (where Pop found his skeleton) was the important island. "Don't you see, you silly boy, that Beacon Island couldn't possibly be Batavia's Graveyard because the Predikant's letter *distinctly* mentions a beach for the little boats. Beacon hasn't got a beach. The fishermen have told me so. Goss Island [two miles from Beacon] is the place. It has a beach. I've seen it myself from the air." I argued rather grumpily that it all depended on your definition of a beach . . . Whether you meant sand a mile wide with a pier and pony rides and Punch and Judy shows, or simply a strand of sorts. Beacon had a strand. I had seen it myself. Henrietta remained unconvinced.

The failure stuck in my craw, but it did us no harm. It merely knocked overboard some of our conceit and overconfidence with cold doses of reality. And our reconnoitering of the reefs and islands was to prove invaluable another day.

In the meantime, I went back to the Mediterranean again.

Ted Falcon-Barker, a rather swashbuckling Australian who ran a diving charter service and had written a book entitled *1600 Years Under the Sea,* wrote to suggest we go to the West Indies to look for the wreck of a fabulous Spanish galleon with the impressive name, *La Nuestra Señora de la Concepción,* which was wrecked in 1641. Why didn't I drop in on him in Spain and talk about it? Why not? I thought. From the look in the editor's eye, I wasn't going to dive for any wrecks in home waters for a long time. The office doors swung open easily.

I arrived on the white wharf at Ibiza a few weeks later, blinking in the strong sunlight. It was July, 1961. Ted's boat *Pagan* was moored alongside some big, broad-hipped Spanish prawn trawlers drying their nets out. He appeared on deck wearing only a pair of tight black swimming trunks and a wide smile.

"Welcome aboard!" he said.

La Nuestra Señora de la Concepción was one of the great lost treasure ships of the world—a legendary galleon. She had been one of those ships which, once a year in annual convoy, carried the loot the Spaniards pillaged from the New World to Spain—the gold and silver of Mexico and Peru, and the bartered bargains from the East, brought from Manila to the Isthmus of Panama in similar galleons.

They were ponderous vessels. In their efforts to thwart the Protestant "Devils" of Buccaneers, the Catholic shipbuilders of the King of Spain built the galleons like great castles. Their sides were studded with gunports, and a saint or cross was painted on every sail, invoking heavenly protection on the high seas. But God also made the waves; the great weight of the armament of brass and iron cannon, and the towering wooden ramparts made the galleons top-heavy, with the result that the sea captured more of them than buccaneers ever boarded.

La Nuestra Señora was one of these.

She sailed with the fleet of 1641, loaded with bars of Peruvian silver, ingots of Mexican gold, chests of coin, Manila spices, Chinese carved ivory and jade, Japanese silks and Indian rubies and precious stones. The wealth was fabulous, fantastic—and it went with the ship to the bottom of the sea in a Caribbean hurricane. Forty years later an American adventurer, William Phipps, found the wreck and salvaged some tons of treasure from her top deck (brought up there presumably before she sank); but Indian divers without breathing gear could not break through to the greater wealth below decks. The wreck was lost again and the treasure remained sunk among the Carib corals.

"I don't know how we'll go about finding it," Ted said frankly. "The hardest thing will be to raise money for an expedition." I grinned ruefully. I'd been on enough expeditions to be familiar with that particular problem. Though we both knew that the chances of finding the wreck were remote, even the faintest barnacle's whisker of a chance made the idea attractive. There was wonderful diving in those clear, bright, Caribbean waters, we had heard. . . .

But we never did get to the West Indies.

While we were spending pleasant weeks loafing around, diving on the wreck of a rather nondescript Roman galley Ted was excavating for the Spanish Government at Ibiza, Cupid caught me off balance—aided by moonlit nights and Spanish champagne, in San Antonio Abad. There were no gentle pricks with tiny arrows, just a hefty sandbag wallop behind the ear. Instead of going to search for the golden galleon, I married a London model named Jenny Lejeune, whom I'd met aboard Ted's boat while she was holidaying in Spain. The overwhelming suddenness of it astonished us both.

So, in place of the trade winds rustling in the palm trees of the far Caribbean, I entered an old stone English church in Bromley, Kent, on a damp, dripping, December day, and heard the preacher pronounce us man and wife.

15 WHALES AND WRECKS

Marriage naturally brought with it a change in my way of life. Back in Australia on my first day at the office the editor eyed me triumphantly. "You'll really have to settle down *now*," he said. "A married man has responsibilities."

But my wife, in addition to her other endearing qualities, was understanding, and I still managed to find time for diving. In odd moments I schemed to get back to the Abrolhos. It took time, but in March, 1963—a few weeks after the birth of our son Christopher—I was once again swimming down, skimming over the old familiar staghorn corals and watching the albacore and snapper finning like flocks of wheeling birds down the 45-degree slope of an Abrolhos reef into the blue depths below. The first time or the hundred-and-first, there is always something new and beautiful in coral waters.

I had persuaded West Australian Newspapers to send an expedition to the wreck of the Dutch ship *Zeewyk,* which was wrecked in 1727, nearly 100 years after the *Batavia,* on the reef near which the *Sardam* had drifted one entire night, fearfully within earshot of the breakers. We had got from a Dutch scholar named B. Goppel in Rotterdam, a copy of the log written by the steersman of the *Zeewijk,* Adriaan de Graaf, telling of the wreck and the nine months spent by the castaway crew on the islands building their sloop of wreck wood to sail to Java with the *Zeewyk*'s treasure. Secretly I hoped to sneak off for a day or two if the opportunity occurred and have another underwater look in that tantalizing area around Beacon Island, fifty miles to the north.

When we arrived in the islands of the southern group aboard George Travia's crayfish carrier boat *Lady Joyous,* fisherman Maurie Glazier—an old diving companion from Shark Bay—was there, waving his arms to indicate the enormous size and girth of something. As we got closer we were able to understand what he meant.

"WHALES. . . ! ! !"

Two humpback whales, he said—a cow and her calf—were in a reef-locked lagoon, trapped there by the tides. They were bottled-up in a natural aquarium where we could inspect them at leisure—see how they dived, rolled, surfaced, propelled their vast bulk through the water . . . a wonderful opportunity!

Would we like to dive in the lagoon with them? Maurie asked.

Would we!

Whales are normally deep-sea creatures and few divers have ever swum with them. The diver who had seen for a few fleeting seconds the great barrel flanks of a passing whale was considered exceptionally fortunate. And now we had the chance to swim, for hours if we liked, with this cow and calf. It was a unique experience, an opportunity perhaps no other divers had ever had. We were a little apprehensive about them at first; after all, the mother was forty feet long and weighed forty tons. In longboat whaling days, whales had shivered longboats and broken the bodies of their crews by flailing in fury with their huge tails, sending harpoons and lines and splintered wood flying. But as it turned out, we had nothing to fear. There was never any danger of being run down—the whales got out of *our* way.

Whales have built-in direction-finding apparatus, nature's sonar, and like porpoises can travel at maximum speed through a dark ocean avoiding all obstacles. Their eyes, set far back on the sides of their heads and almost ridiculously small, are secondary organs. We found the efficiency of their directional sense extraordinary. The mother whale demonstrated her knowledge of our position in the lagoon by weaving under and around groups of divers with tight precision. When we tried to block her path to see her better, she turned in her own length, showing incredible agility and maneuverability for such a huge beast, and gave us a view of a white belly as big as a movie screen. The calf kept station a few feet above her back and copied her every turn, never allowing itself to become separated from her. Occasionally we heard noises like a creaking door—perhaps the whales' sonar "beep."

My first sight of the mother was dramatic—a huge, dark shape nearly as big as a railway locomotive and moving about the same speed . . . She burst into my vision with her huge mouth opening and shutting, showing the rows of baleen brushes through which she strained her dinner of shrimp and plankton. With bubbles creaming off the longitudinal wrinkles on her back, she thundered past me, viewing me fleetingly with her little eye. I dived toward her, but by the time I had traveled a few feet below the surface she was already past, her huge tail, twelve feet across, thumping into the distance, leaving me bobbing in her eddies. All over the lagoon divers were popping up two feet out of the water with incredulous expressions, shouting and waving. "Here she comes—there she goes!" was the cry.

For a time we shepherded mother and calf in Maurie Glazier's fourteen-foot de Havilland aluminum reef boat, while Maurie Hammond took pictures of the auspicious event. Glazier believed that the Mother had deliberately brought her twenty-two-foot, 3000-lb. "baby" into the lagoon as protection against ocean predators—killer whale packs, or those giant orange-eyed white sharks, species Carcharodon—which may have been on the prowl outside the reefs. It was astonishing how gracefully the whales moved. I'd always imagined them as rather ungainly and cumbersome, like elephants and rhinoceros. But their movements were easy, with a fluid surge, and an extra thrust of tail would double their speed without apparent effort. They were gentle, shy creatures, and there was a note of sadness about our meeting with them.

Humpbacks are easily run down and harpooned because of their placid nature and liking for sheltered coastal waters (unlike their squid-eating cousins the sperm whales, which spout in the centrai ocean). Scientifically known as Megaptera nodosa, the humpbacks range from the Arctic to the Antarctic, including the subtropical waters. Just after World War II—during the war men were too busy killing each other to prey on other forms of life—the humpback herds on the Western Australian coast were huge, estimated at 12,000 to 17,000 individuals. Then the whaling started. By 1949, when the Western Australian whaling stations began operations, they were already reduced to 10,000 by the Norwegian, Russian, and British whalers in Antarctica. The Japanese also entered the field and soon the explosions of the harpoon guns echoed all day long in the Antarctic redwater slaughter. And when it came time for the poor hunted whales to swim north to mate in the warm Indian Ocean, the Australian gunners were waiting, crouched over *their* guns. The result was inevitable. By 1963 the Western Australian humpback herd had only 600 survivors—only 600 out of what may have numbered 17,000, and in less than half the lifespan of one whale.

Fortunately the dwindling herd produced its own ironic solution. The whalers, unable to catch enough whales, went broke. The little rusty ships with their high bows, crowlike harpoon guns, and barrels on their masts—from which the cry "THAR SHE BLO-O-O-OWS!" had spelled the death of so many whales—were tied up forlornly, two and three together in harbors, and no one would buy them for there were no more whales. When this happened—such is the way of man—the International Whaling Commission stirred itself, anxiously noted that the humpback herds were "depleted" and protected them. Near extinction, they were at last safe from the guns. By the time the herds have bred back to the stage where it would be economic to hunt them again, let us hope that whale oil (used for lipsticks, synthetics, high-grade machine oils, soap, fats, etc.) will be as out of date as the spinning wheel.

None of us, after watching the mother love of the cow for her calf, could feel anything but sadness at the thought of it all terminating in the blood-stained turmoil following the explosion of a harpoon gun. In fact, most of the divers became so involved watching the pair, we practically had to press-gang them to get them back to work.

The *Zeewyk* expedition was a considerable success. We found interesting barnacled relics in the sea, raised two rust-pitted cannon, and dug up some bones, pistol bullets, bottles and bric-a-brac on Gun Island. The expedition also provided some excellent stories, with the whales stealing the scene and gratifying me with an important journalists' prize.* The whales had cost us any chance of taking time off to go north to look for the *Batavia* but, not having any crystal balls along with our coils of air hose, rusted compressor motors, salt-encrusted rubber suits, scratched masks and coral-chewed flippers, we could not foresee that this expedition was to be a prelude to a much greater adventure.

Among our hairy divers, men from all walks of life—Joe Castlehow, Vic Moir, Merv Brown, Maurie Hammond, Brian Stagg, Peter Webster,

* Publisher's note—The 1964 Lovekin Prize for outstanding journalism in Western Australia.

Colin Firmin, Bill Hill, Naoom Haimson, Albert Ottey, Graham Hill, Dave Hunt, John Craig, Reg Sanderson—the sixteenth and last to join the expedition was a fifteen-stone shell collector and dedicated diver from Geraldton named Max Cramer.

One night over a can of beer—our sole luxury—in the salty, sandy camp on an island we had temporarily taken over from an indignant roost of resident seals, he said:

"Where do you think the *Batavia* wreck really *is*?"

This precipitated a general argument among the divers which went on half the night. At the end of it, I said quietly to Max, "I still think she's in the Wallabis and that Beacon Island is the key to it all." We retired to our sleeping bags and slept on it.

Before we wound up the expedition Max made a proposition. He suggested that I turn over all my research material to him, and he, living in Geraldton only thirty miles from the islands, would slip over on weekends and "fossick around a bit." He pointed out, reasonably, that he had his own business as a builder and was independent of office hours. It would be easy for him to dash over to the islands for a day now and then with the crayfish carrier boats, while on the other hand it would be difficult for me to come up 315 miles from the south, for what might very well be another wild goose chase. He would conduct the reconnaissance and if he found anything we would launch a major expedition together.

I hesitated a moment. Naturally I'd have liked the selfish pleasure of being in the first dive on the wreck. This way, Max would have that triumph to himself—supposing that he found anything. But of course there was always the possibility that he'd find it on his own without my research notes. Cooperation was so obviously commonsense that I agreed, and we shook hands on it.

Back in Perth, I posted him up the folder full of dog-eared notes, maps and scribbled theories labeled "BATAVIA" and forgot all about the matter in the dismal, dripping, rain-pelting gloom of the May-to-August southwest Australian winter monsoon.

Then, late one night in June, a radio bulletin came through. "SKIN DIVERS IN THE ABROLHOS ISLANDS HAVE LOCATED THE 334-YEAR-OLD WRECK OF THE DUTCH EAST INDIA COMPANY SHIP BATAVIA. MR. MAX CRAMER OF GERALDTON . . ."

We were at a meeting of our divers' club at the time, and everyone understood when I catapulted from my chair and flung myself on the telephone. "Trunk lines, get me Max Cramer, Geraldton 806," I yelled into its impersonal black plastic receiver.

They had brought back a small cannon and a human skull. The wreck was lying in three fathoms of water on a storm-blasted ledge of dead coral off one of the outer reefs where breakers roared on all but the quietest of days. Dodging into the maelstrom in favorable weather, they had been utterly astonished by what they saw on the sea bottom.

"You should see the bronze cannon!" Max shouted over the phone. "Covered with scrolls and coats of arms . . . Fabulous!"

"You old son-of-a-gun!—where'd you find it?"

He laughed. "I hope you've got a sense of humor. It was only a few hundred yards from where you were swimming in 1960."

"Well I'll be . . . !"

The anchor Kevin McCagh had written to us about was in fact the bow anchor of the *Batavia.* Dave Johnson had come across it while setting crayfish pots later that year. In subsequent visits on calm days, looking through a water glass he had seen square ballast blocks on the bottom and what he correctly believed were cannon. He told no one, but when Max Cramer and his brother Graham came to Beacon Island, Dave decided he had kept the secret long enough, and took them out in his boat to the site. There Max became the first man to dive on the *Batavia* wreck. It was an auspicious date, June 4, 1963—the 334th anniversary of the sinking. Dave also showed them a skull which he'd found while sinking a hole for a post. He hinted at other bones while Max and Graham turned the soil over, using shovels and the sieves from the *Zeewyk* expedition. They found fragments of glass and copper and part of a flintlock pistol mechanism. It seemed certain that Beacon Island, as we had believed, was Batavia's Graveyard!

"How soon can you come up?" asked Max.

"The first aircraft I can grab a seat on!"

We shouted over the static and crackle of the long-distance line—a thunderstorm was raging somewhere along the 315 miles of wire separating us—until the switchboard girl decently chipped in to warn us that the bill had reached alarming proportions. I put the phone down and rang the MacRobertson Miller airline office where a clerk booked a seat for early the next day.

My brain was in a whirl all night. I had visions of giant gray-green waves curling over like cliffs to break on my unprotected head, of sinister things among the corals. I woke up breathless and sweating a number of times before dawn. When the first gray light came, stealing up the garden past the tall palm tree and through the mosquito-net curtains, I lay awake beside the sweetly sleeping form of my wife trying to think what we must do now that the wreck was found.

Obviously we had to mount an expedition to survey the *Batavia* and raise the more valuable relics. This must be done with all speed to forestall pirate divers who might go on the hunt for coins and souvenirs now that the news was out and damage the pristine wreck. It had happened before. And only during the brief spell of calms which was coming at the beginning of August before the equinox would it be possible to work close to the perilous reef. This left us only seven weeks; we would have to work breathlessly fast. The expedition would involve all the usual factors, but on a grander scale because of the importance of the wreck, and more hazardous than normal because of the exposed position in the surf. We had to worry about waves, men, equipment, supplies, and money. . . . Especially money.

Watching an early bird sharpening his beak on the branch of the red-flowering gum tree out in the garden, I mused back over the expeditions I could think of and tried to recall one on which there had *not* been problems with money. "It's practically impossible to get money for expeditions these days . . . Unless someone gets eaten by monsters, or you find a chest of gold—both things rather hard to arrange in advance," Ted Falcon-Baker once said as we stared over *Pagan*'s rail at our reflection in the blue harbor of San Antonio Abad. Money to buy equipment, to pay for gasoline, for compressed air, for boats, for lifting gear, for outboard motors, for food to fill the bellies of hungry divers . . . for the nine hundred and ninety-nine other things necessary to run an expedition of the kind we were planning. A lot of money.

To divert money out of its normal circulatory routes for a different or one-way voyage is extremely difficult, especially where expeditions are concerned—they're uncharted waters. Sadly, the people who really do have money are seldom interested in such obscure pursuits as underwater achaeology. Endow an expedition? Not on your Nellie . . . Unless you bait your hook with the gaudy lure of a tale of fantastic treasure, guarded (of course) by sharks and giant octopi and marked with an X on an ancient tortoise-shell chart given to you by a dying Indian whose life you once saved. But that sort of thing requires a conscience of some elasticity. Since my assets were limited to a battered Willys jeep, miscellaneous diving gear, a few shelves of books in a study arrayed with shark jaws and polished shells, and a faithful, hard-worked typewriter that knew the midnight hours too well, it was obvious that I wasn't going to be able to help our *Batavia* cause much by digging into my own pocket. Neither was Max.

We would just have to hope for something to turn up. So far, something always had.

16 THE EXPEDITION

I flew north to Geraldton in a venerable DC3, an aged, uncomplaining aerial workhorse now relegated to such provincial routes. The sun glinted on the hundreds of rivet heads in its wrinkled old wings, and I prayed earnestly that nothing would fall off. But we made it safely in an agreeably short time, landing in sunshine among green wheat fields.

Max was waiting in shorts and a khaki shirt, with a wide grin. "Good to see you, sport."

"And you."

After the usual greetings we climbed into his olive Volkswagen with red Australian hinterland dust covering the back mudguards and set off for the town four miles away.

He drove fast, with the air-cooled engine behind the back seat revving with the familiar high-pitched VW scream, until we reached the Chinese cemetery on the town boundary and a series of reproving 35-mph signs.

"I suppose you've been doing a lot of thinking," he said.

"That's the understatement of the year."

"What thoughts are turning in the giant brain?" The tone was bantering but his eyes were serious.

"We're going to need a lot more heavy equipment than we've had before. That means heavy money. It's going to be hard work getting hold of it. There'll be no trouble getting good divers. It's the money that's worrying. Pounds, shillings, and pence. The old problem."

"The museum . . . a State Government grant?"

"They're the obvious sources. But the museum hasn't an unlimited budget and generally plans projects a year or so ahead. It may be too much to expect a large grant from them at such short notice, however willing they may be. They'll probably be sympathetic enough to find something, but we'd be overly optimistic if we expected that they'd cover the whole bill."

Max thought that the Geraldton Town Council might assist with a donation. We discussed commercial sources, newspapers, and other possible benefactors. We decided that we would apply for a grant through the museum, and if that failed approach the Philistines—the big business firms which occasionally helped in unusual ventures because of the advertising benefits from playing Big Daddy to mountaineers, solo ocean yachtsmen, world motor speed aspirants, and other crazy characters, into which category we would be lumped, like it or not..

Max made a face. "Breakfast foods . . . Snap, Crackle and Pop with the *Batavia* Pirates . . . I can feel the laxative effect already!"

"Don't look a gift horse in the packet."

We drove past the Shepherds Hotel and the bar of the Victoria Hotel, old stamping grounds on the main street. We talked about divers, agreeing on a nucleus of the experienced fellows from the *Zeewyk*. With a lot to do in a short time, numbers would be important.

"It may even be possible to borrow a squad of Navy divers," I said. "Hec Donohue—the lieutenant in charge of diving at the HMAS Leeuwin shore depot in Fremantle—has mentioned several times that they'd like to help us on a wreck."

"They might be able to supply some of the heavy gear."

"And bring a boat."

Max threaded the beetle bonnet of the Volks through the traffic to the other side of town where the red-and-white striped lighthouse at Point Moore stood out over the mast-spiked horizon of the fisherman's harbor like a sentinel. A tang of salt, bait, fish and rope wafted down the road. "Now you're going to see the first *Batavia* cannon," he said.

The gun they had brought back from the Abrolhos was still aboard the crayfish carrier boat *Emmalou,* tied up alongside the main wharf. Its weight caused a perceptible list on the sixty-six-foot craft. The cannon was short, squat, and green with verdigris, with white patches of coral that were beginning to smell as they dried out. It nestled on a heap of sandbags and old tire fenders. A small knot of fishermen were gathered around it.

"Christ—three-hundred years old!" one of them was saying, patting the barrel with a knotted, calloused hand.

As we reached the edge of the wharf one of the group, a dark-haired man in a blue check shirt and dungarees, looked up and grinned. "What do you think of it?" He was Frank Bombara, skipper of the *Emmalou,* and his grin started somewhere under his right ear and seemed to cut his face in half.

We stepped on to the gunwale and dropped down to the deck to look at the gun more closely.

"See the VOC mark?" said Max, pointing out the famous mark of the great Company. On the breech was indented a ragged letter A and the number 1836, cut in with a hand chisel. He rubbed a hand over it, brushing away some flakes of green verdigris and copper. "The 1836 worried some of the blokes a bit. They thought it was a date, and two-hundred years too late for the *Batavia.*"

"The gun serial number," I reassured him. "The A stands for the Chamber of Amsterdam in the Dutch East India Company—*Batavia* sailed from Amsterdam."

Max looked relieved.

It was an unusual cannon, about five-and-a-half-feet long, made of copper as far as we could tell, with a separate brass knob pinned to the butt with iron spikes to form a sort of tulip bulb which carried the touchhole. Curious. Usually the touchhole was on top of the butt. The distinct acrid smell of gunpowder came from the barrel where sand and coral had been scraped out. They had raised it by sinking 44-gallon fuel drums, lashing them to the gun, and filling the drums with exhaust gases pumped down through a hose from Dave Johnson's diesel engine. When the drums floated again, they lifted the cannon and Dave towed it away below its raft of bobbing drums. After several adventures which included nearly losing it in the 23-fathom channel, they heaved it aboard the *Emmalou,* twenty or so fishermen sweating and straining on the hawsers to parbuckle it over the side. "A gut-busting process," said Frank. History was a considerable weight, they complained.

The cannon was thought-provoking. Where had it been? I wondered. On ships flying the proud red-white-and-blue flag of old Holland, before it bubbled down into the deeps with the wreck of the *Batavia?* Had it flamed broadsides of whistling iron death at English privateers, Barbary brigands, or Sulu Sea pirates? Cannon were major war weapons for more than 400 years. In a book called *Fabulous Voyage**—a fabulous tale of two Bristol privateers called the *Duke* and *Duchess* which sailed around the world and in 1709 captured one of the legendary Spanish Manila galleons—there is a powder-pungent passage about cannons.

The big guns were substantially the same as those of the 16th and 17th centuries. Some were cast of iron, others of brass, others wrought iron. Because of inevitable and understandable flaws in their manufacture they might blow up the first time they were fired, or the fiftieth, or the two hundredth, and each or any or every time the gunner put the flaming linstock to the touch-hole, no one knew what would happen. All the guns jumped violently when hot, sometimes snapping their breaching and slamming back into a bulk-head, sometimes overturning, sometimes leaping up into the beams overhead. And in any extended action, if they were not allowed to cool off for a couple of hours—no matter how much sluicing and bathing and washing they got and how much sponging with cold water and vinegar between shots—any or all of them would burst . . .

The guns could not be aimed with any great accuracy; they had to be traversed or elevated or depressed by hand; moreover the iron round shot generally did not closely fit the barrels. Therefore, although cannon balls might travel several miles effective sea-fights were carried on at a range of no more than a quarter mile and at the optimum the point-blank range for flintlock muskets . . . All that weight of leaping, bucking red-hot metal the gunners had to fight and avoid in a swirling darkness where they could barely see in batteries choked and blanketed by the smoke of black powder.

Sea fights were grim indeed. From the time Drake fought the galleons of the Armada in 1588 until Nelson died in his hour of triumph aboard his shot-splintered flagship *Victory* at Trafalgar in 1805, they were conducted along much the same lines. Like two blood-spattered boxers standing toe-to-toe, they slammed punches until one or both fell from the damage of the blows or sheer exhaustion. Glory was a bloody affair and the victors often as badly mauled as the vanquished. The ships fought at point-blank range in a stinking smog of smoke and gunpowder fumes, throwing red-hot metal until a lucky shot disabled one or the other, or until casualties mounted so high they were unable to continue. The gun ports were painted red, as were the gun

* *Fabulous Voyage,* F. MacLiesh and M. Krieger, Gollancz, London, 1963.

decks, to minimize the horror of blood sluicing through the scuppers. They kept tubs of sand at strategic intervals so that the gunners would not slip in their comrades' blood. Officers stood by with pistols to shoot anyone who deserted his post. They fired red-hot shot to set the enemy afire; shot joined together with chains to cut his rigging; balls joined with bars to cut his masts; and "grape"—small shot and ragged lumps of iron— to rip the bellies and life out of their opposing gunners. Casualties were high, and the odds of the wounded surviving lessened by the surgeons, whose lack of medical knowledge was notorious, in an age where anaesthetics were unknown, and sterilizing instruments unheard of. As much damage to human life and limb was done by splinters of woodwork which ricocheted about the decks, and falling masts and spars, as from the shrieking iron shot. Despite strategically slung nets filled with blankets, bedding and hammocks, these took a heavy toll. The hope of every skipper was to grapple alongside the enemy before too much damage was done and board him with cutlass and pike. This was better than getting shot to bits, and the winner usually had a prize in the other vessel which the crew shared in by tradition—so that they were enthusiastic about these encounters on the high seas in an age where life was cheap and they were as likely to be struck down by scurvy or smallpox or syphilis as a cannon ball. Perhaps this *Batavia* gun had seen the sulphurous hell of an old-time gun deck in action.

Max's voice brought me back to the deck of the fishing boat in 1963. There were immediate and practical matters to attend to, and I had to fly back that afternoon.

The cannon was lifted ashore by a mobile crane, while we watched, to be taken to a place of exhibition. Max and I put our heads together for the rest of the day.

"I've done my bit, mate; it's your turn now," he said as he drove me out to the airport again.

Organizing expeditions is an exhausting business, most of it downright drudgery made bearable only by the thought of the goal ahead. During the weeks before the *Batavia* expedition I often dreamed of the sea. How cool to glide down in clear, green depths, among the corals and the rainbow fish below the silver ceiling of the surface above, and escape . . . But there was no reprieve. I worked until 2 A.M. most nights, arriving at work next day red-eyed and wretched. I had to write dozens of letters; organize everything from boats to bottles of ketchup; see innumerable officials; deal with some very helpful and some very stupid people; carry on a one-man publicity campaign on behalf of the expedition; convince the cynics; sway the doubters; restrain the too-enthusiastic. In the end, my folder of letters, lists and notes weighed nearly as much as a diver's lead belt, and I had the feeling that the whole expedition hung on the drawstring of my soul, like that dead albatross around the Ancient Mariner's neck. But in less than six weeks we scraped together more than forty men, two seventy-five-foot craft, each worth about £75,000 with their gear, a mountain of diving equipment, and enough money to meet our immediate needs. In the process my nerves were rubbed red-raw and I became as irritable as a shark with a sore jaw—snapping at floating tins, pieces of timber, or anything bobbing by. But somehow the work had been completed.

The easiest part of it all was recruiting divers. Hec Donohue reacted enthusiastically to the suggestion of bringing his Navy group and wangled a seventy-five-foot workboat and a raft of drums from Navy Stores for lifting the cannon. When the Army Special Air Service divers heard about it, they wanted to come, too. They would bring their own boat, the *Lerida*. It was becoming embarrassing. We had our own band of skilled civilian divers, most of whom had worked on the *Zeewyk* and other wrecks, were familiar with Abrolhos conditions, and could handle themselves in turbulent white water—necessary for survival in the surf of the wreck site. They were also compatible—an important factor. Those tense fiction dramas of men at each other's throats in an Arctic hut or a desert tent have a grim basis in fact. When men are in continual close contact in isolation from the rest of the world, strange neuroses set in. They become a little mad. Things that would seem too trivial to bother about in normal living become incidents of the first magnitude. There is the story of a scientific man of renown who, after brooding for weeks, attacked a camp cook with a cleaver because he had been getting soft- instead of hard-boiled eggs. And there is a frightful but true tale of a man thrown overboard at sea because he stole his mate's razor blades. Those are extreme cases. But even seemingly normal, healthy, happy men can become brooding and surly on an island, finding fault with the expedition and each other until things really begin to go wrong. The selection of his men is any expedition leader's gravest responsibility, and it follows that keeping them happy once in the field is his most important job. This is no new problem, of course, as any ship's captain or army colonel will tell you. It bothered Alexander the Great, and the Romans wrote treatises about it. Certainly Francisco Pelsaert's ghost would have had much to say on the matter. He wrote, as the *Sardam* returned to Java with survivors and prisoners: "For the first time I can clearly see and realise that a human being often finds his worldly welfare has fallen into the hands of 2 or 3 perfidious men . . ." We were to be more fortunate.

For operational purposes we had three leaders: Max Cramer, Lieutenant Donohue, and me. Lieutenant P. Caskey skippered the Army workboat *Lerida*. Max was a competent man at most things he tackled, whether building houses, raising cannon, or collecting shells (his collection of gleaming cowries and volutes was among the finest in Australia, and he corresponded and traded with fellow conchologists all over the world). He was twenty-eight at the time of the expedition, had two children, a house on a hill in Geraldton stuffed with shells and marine curiosities, and a partly-painted lounge room that had been that way for two years because his frequent good intentions about it (to his wife's exasperation) were continually diverted by diving. Official photographer would be Maurie Hammond. He was the best underwater photographer in Western Australia and, we believed at that time, the best in Australia. He was a character—small, with wispy, rapidly-thinning hair, a sun-wrinkled forehead, excellent teeth, and a gift for garrulous, colorful and sometimes wildly exaggerated anecdote. He was as sharp as a sniper with his camera. Then there was Merv Brown, the boffin (scientific expert) of the outfit. The breathing apparatus, the electronic metal detector and the explosives (we didn't want any one-armed or one-legged divers) were his responsibility—as well as any other jobs that required delicate touch and a little genius. Once on the *Zeewyk* expedition when his automatic Japanese camera broke, Merv, a neat man with a neat moustache and serious eye, sat down on a beach with tweezers, screwdriver and clean handkerchief and pulled the fearfully complicated thing apart. He ground a new ball bearing out of the head of a pin and put it back together so that it worked perfectly. "Impossible," said professional camera mechanics when we told them later. But I saw him do it.

George Brenzi, who had Rudolph Valentino eyes and a permanently sleepy expression, was engineer. Despite his appearance he was in fact singularly alert and had a ready and imperturbable wit. He was a transport operator, and after jockeying big trucks over crowded highways, nothing shook him. I only saw him ruffled once—on another wreck when someone detonated a high explosive charge while he was in the water nearby. Even then he was milder about it than I have often been when I've hit my thumb with a hammer. He was a very cool, sure operator underwater. Jack Sue, another of the band, had once been a secret agent and had a cloak-and-dagger past as an Allied spy behind Japanese lines in Borneo during the war. He was Australian-Chinese, spoke fluent Malay, and he had disguised himself as a coolie without difficulty and gained valuable information on Japanese installations and the whereabouts of thousands of prisoners-of-war whose fate until then had been unknown. In the process, he had killed men with his bare hands.

There was always the unspoken fear of a serious accident at the back of our minds. The man whose skill we hoped we'd never really need was Naoom Haimson, our doctor. He was a diver too, of course, as they all were. He was a short, barrellike chap with a bristling beard, twinkling eyes, and a black pipe that smelled as though its combustion processes involved old motor tires and camel urine. We touched wood (all divers are superstitious) that he would never have to perform an emergency operation on those isolated islands. The Western Australian Museum was sending Chris Halls, their ships, arms and armor expert; West Australian Newspapers released David Tanner to assist with the photography; Max's brother Graham, ex-American Air Force man Cal Hoven, and Greg Allen would join us in Geraldton. Dave Johnson was waiting in the Abrolhos.

We were lucky with equipment. Thanks to Commodore W. Marks of HMAS *Leeuwin,* the *GPV* * *958* was cleared for the expedition, raft and other gear provided. Commercial equipment manufacturers were generous. De Havilland Marine Australia gave us an aluminum surf tender with BATAVIA EXPEDITION lettered on the side, which was to prove invaluable. Outboard Marine Australia contributed an 18-horsepower Evinrude. Airdive Australia helped with aqualungs and rubber suits, and Jean Richard made underwater timepieces available at ridiculously low cost. By the time we were ready to leave, we had every item of gear we could reasonably require.

Money remained a problem to the end. The museum people were

* General Purpose Vessel—light cargo ship/minesweeper/patrol craft/troop carrier.

as helpful as they could be. Director Dr. David Ride, his assistant director Dr. R. George, and the Curator of Archaeology Mr. I. Crawford pressed our case and tried hard to get us a decent grant through government sources. We celebrated prematurely when a select committee, set up by the Government to advise them, recommended that we should get £1000. But in the end the grant was cut down to a parsimonious £250 by officialdom in the Treasury. They neglected to tell us until the day before the expedition sailed—giving us no time to campaign for funds in other directions—and we were furious. Fortunately the Geraldton Council came to the rescue with a further £250 and we were able to scrape by. In the early stages I had to run the expedition on my own bank overdraft account—something which would have sent my bank manager into convulsions if he'd known.

As every day passed, we became more and more impatient to get to the wreck. And then, at last, we were ready.

17 REEFS LIKE A SAVAGE'S NECKLACE

The reefs on which the *Batavia* was wrecked are strung around the two large Wallabi Islands like a sharp-tooth necklace around a savage's neck. They are marked in white lines of breakers and spouts and flashes of foam where the swells of the deep blue Indian Ocean come up against the submarine battlements of the reefs. Behind the shelter of the reefs are the greens, browns, and yellows of the shallows, and the limpid lagoons where seals bask.

There are three main coils of reefs; three foam-shrouded sisters. The men of HMS *Beagle* named them Morning, Noon, and Evening Reefs in 1840, because of the order in which the sun passes over them —rising behind Morning, beating brassily down on Noon at midday, and sinking in golden, red-flecked sunset behind Evening. It was hungry Morning which claimed the life of the *Batavia* 211 years before their visit.

The outer islands, of which Batavia's Graveyard was one, are strung around the reef perimeter like knots in the necklace, appearing as irregular blobs on the map or from an airplane. Seen from the sea, they are lizardlike silhouettes, so low that you wonder why the storm waves of the occasional hurricanes do not riot across them, sluicing the scraggy bushes, birds' nests, nodding salt daisies and all to perdition in the deep channels. But the sea keeps to its boundaries, though it sometimes snarls and threatens these upstart pocket-handkerchief pieces of earth.

The islands are formed by the heaping up of coral shale and sand at spots of conflicting currents on the plateaus of the shallows. Plants sprout from seeds in seabird droppings and bind the sand with root and tendril, preventing it from blowing or washing away and holding together islands one evolutionary stage above a sandbank. Batavia's Graveyard, now Beacon Island, is one of these. A mile south of it in the foam of the reef lies the wreck.

If you had a mind to, and had a stout pair of boots against the brittle and sharp corals, you could wade—crushing staghorn, brittle star, sea slug, urchin and shell under heel—through the reef shallows in a semicircle south to the wreck site, close enough to fling a stone onto the forepart of the wreck. On the way you would pass the platform of rock surmounted by a few determined bushes which the Dutch called Traitor's Island. The castaway Hollanders had waded and poled their rafts around the shallows from islet to islet, salvaging floating barrels of salt pork and wine, and wood to make their beach-built scows. Ariaen Jacobsz and the seamen, in their all-too-brief time at the wreck, had steered in the deep channel separating Batavia's Graveyard and Seal's Island, mistrusting the cross-currents and the lumps and spikes of coral in the shallows which reached up for boats' keels. Modern boats for the same reason pass the same way. Down the 23-fathom channel from the anchorages behind the reefs out to the heaving swells of the open ocean, fishing boats sail at dawn to work their myriad crayfish pots, dotting the sea with hundreds of bobbing white marker floats with flags waving atop the first and last floats in the lines as markers.

The way to the wreck for boats is from the deep sea, turning about on the old course of the *Batavia,* and coming northeast from the indigo deeps to where the corals first appear misty gray below and the big swells begin to hump and throw their chests out as they approach the submarine cliff of the reef. On a rough day when the ocean is angry any approach to the wreck becomes impossible. The site is wild in a boil of spume. Hollow thirty-foot combers roll with smoking tops from half a mile out to explode in spouts of spray. Their thunder carries threateningly on the wind, the shallows tremble, and a seething cauldron of white water lips the reefs. But there are other days when the seas are sunny-gentle and only a curtain lace of foam runs across the reef, the ocean moving with a barely perceptible heave of its bosom that is no more than a sigh. These are a few days a year, rare jewel days when sea and sky are equally blue and only the faintest ruffle of wind comes and dies away again in the afternoon. On days like this, and sometimes too when the wind runs around to the north and the ocean becomes sullen and leaden-calm before a big storm, it is possible to sail right over the wreck in a small boat—as the steward Reynder Hendricx did when he told Pelsaert he had touched money chests with a pike—though even on the calm water caution is necessary. Sometimes the sea will be still, hour after hour, and then with no warning a line of three or more big waves will march in out of the ocean and break in fathom-deep white froth on a front a mile wide. Now and then modern fishermen who forget or relax their vigilance are caught by breakers, and are smashed, overturned, and swallowed up by the waves which roar triumphantly over them—just as they took *Sardam* skipper Jacob Jacobsz and his sloop crew so long ago.

Below the surface the scene is so peaceful and beautiful that to a diver the boisterous surge and swirl above seems scarcely possible. In the silence below the tight silver skin of the surface the corals are stacked tier upon tier, ledges and castles, with submarine canyons and sudden descents plunging away into the mystery of unseen depths. The shallows are bright with color where the sun strikes through the surface: blue and green coral, red sponges, mauve anemones, golden fans, rainbow fish in improbable coats of many colors, orange inquisitive antennae of crayfish protruding like straws from under ledges, withdrawing as the diver's shadow passes over. . . . Schools of restless, pelagic fish—tuna, mackerel, skipjack, kingfish—patrol the deep channel edges endlessly. The sinister shadow of a shark passes once in a while, patiently waiting for one of the school fish to turn the wrong way into ready jaws. The rock fish fin and circle in their own limited kingdoms, never venturing far, always ready to dash back to their lairs in corals and crevasses. One eye fixed on their shelter, the other rolls inquisitively at the human intruders—strange creatures peering through the misty glass of face masks, tight black rubber suits clamped on chest, thigh and wrist, trailing strings of bubbles like pearls, and filling the underwater amphitheater with the harsh echo of labored breathing from the apparatus strapped on their backs. Moving with heavy strokes of fins, they seem large grotesque birds, flying, arms outstretched, heavily under the sea. . . . Down they swim, down into the deep water where the corals become less exotic and the colors fade as the depth takes away the reds and yellows from the spectrum until everything becomes a misty magic blue with iridescent glows and fires. They pause on the brink and look down into the twilight of the Very Deep . . . 300 feet, 500 feet, 1000 feet, where men may not go. . . .

We steamed into the lee of East Wallabi Island near sunset on July 28, 1963. Leading was the Royal Australian Navy's *GPV 958,* at seventy-five feet very nearly as big and long as the *Sardam.* Stocky and square, and very Navy in her gray paint, her wheelhouse was mounted like a sentry box on the superstructure amidships, with a single mast forward, and a derrick for raising cannon. She was a portly, middle-aged vessel with six knots of puffing dignity, a brass telegraph that went CLANG CLANG with as much importance as the *Queen Mary,* and a hooter that roared with stentorian authority. The Dutch would have liked her portentous stolidity. Impatiently in her wake came the Army's *Lerida.* Of similar size, she was different in appearance with her wheelhouse forward, a high bow and low, square stern trawler-style, and wore dark olive green with a big white AS 1739 on her bow. She was much smarter, faster and more modern.

Both craft had their holds stuffed tight and their decks stacked high with diving equipment and stores in crates, boxes and sacks. Civilian divers in blue denim pants and roll-neck sweaters, seamen in blue shorts and white square-necked Navy shirts, and green-jacketed soldiers, squeezed in where they could find room, passing cigarettes and chocolates, reading paperbacks and yarning. Long before we sighted the islands they were peering ahead with interest and anticipation.

East Wallabi first appeared as a broken horizon line of dots which swelled, humped, and in a short time joined together to become an island. It was another half-hour before we saw the outlines of other, lower islands and the white breakers around them. We surged in through the reefs, passing on our way the hill where Pelsaert had stared with a wonder that turned to horror as Weibbe Hayes grounded his little boat and ran up the beach gasping news of mutiny and murders. Once through the gateway we swung sou'west to bear down on the silhouette of that island . . . Batavia's Graveyard in 1629, today called Beacon Island.

"Prepare to drop anchor!" Hec Donohue bawled, and a crew of ratings scurried about the foredeck wrestling with the heavy anchor.

Arthur Pearse, a Fisheries Inspector loaned to the Navy as pilot because of his knowledge of the reef waters, leaned on the brass binnacle beside Hec, squinting professionally into the sinking sun. Abrolhos reefs rose abruptly from the sea floor, some rearing from twenty-three fathoms (138 ft.) to knee depth in less than twenty yards. We eyed the darkening water ahead nervously. Arthur seemed unconcerned, secure in his knowledge.

Max took the binoculars. "Here comes Dave Johnson," he said.

A small speck detached itself from behind the low island and came hurrying towards us in a fleck of white spray. Little puffs of spray bounced as the boat jolted towards us, traveling fast. Soon we heard the sound of a high-powered outboard motor on the wind, and quite suddenly Dave Johnson was beside us, tossing unevenly on the swell. The little boat with its high cabin forward was typical of the crayfishing scooter boats. He had a big 40-horse Evinrude outboard on an iron bracket at the stern and a faithful chugging diesel inboard for economical work on the fishing grounds. The boat smelled of bait and diesel oil. Grayfish bags hung near the winch.

Her skipper was young and fair, his face red-brown, his green waterproofs gleaming with spray. Standing on the stern he worked the tiller with one sea-booted foot and kicked the outboard motor out of gear with a practiced backward motion of the other as he drew level. The fishing registration number G70 had been painted in big irregular white letters with a hasty brush on the bow. He waved.

"Good . . ." he cried, balancing expertly, the wind whipping the rest of his words away before they reached us. His young wife Petra, scarf around her head, peered cautiously from the dry shelter of the cabin and waved, keeping out of the spray, and ducked back in again. A dog stood with his forefeet on the gunnel and barked. The boat rocked wildly in the mid-channel wave chop. Then Dave was off again, signaling us to follow.

The ponderous craft dipped solemnly in his wake towards Beacon Island and turned obediently at the anchorage he indicated. Splash! went the anchors; rumble! went the chains.

"Finished with engines!" shouted Hec Donohue down the engine room voice tube.

"Ding-Ding," the telegraph answered.

There was sudden quiet as the thudding diesel of the GPV cut into silence. We were there.

The divers looked south to the line of foam that marked the wreck reef on the darkening ocean. Their eyes were shining.

My first impression was that the cannon was glowing gold. It lay there nestled among green leaves of cabbage coral, with one clump of very blue brain coral growing up near its butt across the scrollwork decorating the old bronze. The water—about twenty feet deep—was very clear. I remember noting the color contrasts with pleasure . . . the yellow, green and blue, and some little red fish that kept flickering inquisitively from under and around the cannon. Later I discovered that the yellow was really a surface reflection of dappled sunlight from the rippled waves above, and the cannon was really more green than gold. But such is the strength of first impressions that now when I close my eyes and remember that scene under the boil of the surf, the cannon is still yellow as all the gold in the King's counting house.

It was an incredible, almost hysterical day. So much happened that I clean forgot that it was July 29—my thirtieth birthday—and the memory of the events even now is a little confused. In my diary I wrote simply: "We went to the wreck. . . ." I could never have put down the belly-twisting, heart-jarring excitement that it really meant.

During the morning we had unloaded our gear onto Beacon Island, toting it patiently on our shoulders from the beach like a procession of ants carrying grains of sugar. The island hadn't changed much in the three years since we had last been there. It was still smaller than a football field, grown over with gnarled salt shrubs, lapped on all sides by the waves. There were a few more crayfish pots, one more jetty spider-legging out into the shallows, and the lines of bait racks had extended slightly along the foreshore; but it still had its four huts, the Bevilaquas—Bill and Grace—Pop Marten, Alan Martin and his wife Myrtle still occupying them, and they made us as welcome as before. But now the soil beneath our feet had a new significance. I saw Maurie Hammond staring thoughtfully at the ground. Few corners of Australia could match in macabre horror the things that had happened on this little island.

When we crunched up the path of white coral to the huts, Dave Johnson greeted us cheerily. "There are a whole lot of skeletons under here," he said, tapping the concrete floor of his sprawling many-roomed asbestos-walled shack with a seabooted foot. The divers crowded around him with their dufflebags, wide-eyed. "I only put the concrete down a couple of weeks ago," he added, enjoying their expressions. "Pity you weren't earlier. You could have had a lot of fun digging them up."

We stared at the floor. This was where we would be sleeping on stretchers and air mattresses; cheek to cheek with dead men.

"Anyone believe in ghosts?" Max asked.

"Someone give me a hand with these regulators," shouted Merv Brown from the beach.

We had to quell our excitement with a physical effort and force ourselves to get the work finished. Eyes kept turning south to the line of foam that marked the reef. THE reef.

At last the unloading was complete. Stiff-fingered with impatience we pulled on the tight-fitting diving suits, smelling the rubbery newness of them. We walked awkwardly down to the beach, each man armored like the Black Prince. We adjusted the aqualung valves and harness, checked anchor lines and fuel gauges, and pulled the starting toggles of the outboard motors clamped on the transoms of the de Havilland aluminum coral-proof boats (the fishermen had lent us two twelve-footers as additions to our fleet) until the engines roared and spluttered. Fiddling with our rubber helmets and mask straps, we throttled back the impatience. At last everyone was ready.

The divers in black suits and helmets looked like longship Viking warriors in silhouette against the sun as the boats dipped out through the shallows into the deep channel to take for the first time that long sweep south and east—to the wreck. My heart thumped painfully, and I could see Max's face creased with the same strain. Seeing me, he grinned unconvincingly.

Then Dave Johnson, one knotted arm resting casually on the cray hoist of his boat, looked across at ours, pointed and shouted through the puff of exhaust: "There she is!" He kicked his motor out of gear and went forward to the anchor.

Splash! Splash! Splash! Divers hit the water from his boat before he had stopped, adjusting masks and straps and bubbling air and foam as they disappeared below the surface, dark blurs, quickly vanishing. We cast our anchor hastily.

I sprang awkwardly from the gunwale. Horizon and boats canted crazily and when I jumped I swallowed a mouthful of sea water in my eagerness. I sank in the first blind moment, tugged down by my lead weights, and jerked at my harness to set the cylinder of compressed air on my back. Comfortably sucking air through the mouthpiece clamped between my teeth, I strained through the foam and bubbles caused by my own turmoil in entering the water to see what lay below my flippers. Corals appeared distantly. I turned over and began to dive towards them, watching the bottom come up.

Then I saw the first cannon, lying among the green fronds and fingers of coral, with some little red-striped fish peering out inquisitively from under and around it. I had often imagined this scene. Strangely—for mind-pictures are often fanciful and wide of the mark—it was almost as I had dreamed it. I floated over the cannon for a long time, balancing with kicks of my fins against the current, studying its length, noting the trunnions. A section of my mind shrieked crazily out of gear with excitement, while another department dispassionately noted the measurements and appearance of the cannon. It was eleven feet long, I calculated; massive, with scrollwork and a coat of arms which disappeared under encroaching coral wreaths and garlands. I chipped gently with a knife, as a school of kingfish flashed silver in the background, and uncovered the word "Rotterdam" and the date 1616. It had two ornamented dolphins as handles and a fish lived in the barrel.

Most of us have supreme moments in our lives. Sir Edmund Hillary had his when he stood with Sherpa Tensing on the top of Everest after breaking through the last barrier of snow and ice, the first men to climb the world's highest mountain. The rest of us have lesser Everests. Mine was that cannon on the *Batavia,* and looking at it I felt like weeping into my face mask for joy.

It was the sure sign that we had reached our goal.

18 DON'T EXPECT TO SEE A GALLEON IN FULL SAIL

Wrecks are usually not a bit like the popular image of a sunken ship. "Don't expect to see a galleon in full sail on the bottom," I warned the divers at the pre-expedition briefing. It takes an astonishingly short time for the sea to make a ruin of a fine vessel. What happens after a sinking depends a good deal on the location of the wreck. In the turbulent, tide-racked waters of the English Channel it will be wrenched viciously apart in a few months and widespread fragments will sink into the sands, perhaps miles from each other, like scattered bones. In contrast, in the black, still Baltic it may hang together in the silent, near-freshwater deeps for hundreds of years. And the blue, limpid Mediterranean is also kind to sunken ships.

On the Australian coast it is likely that a ship will founder in surf or vigorously moving water. With wooden ships, the masts go almost immediately. Deckhouses and superstructures swirl into collapse with the subtle but tremendous forces of tides and currents. The sun-warmed water stimulates rapid sea-growth. Soon the hull is hung with weeds, algae and bright corals. A billion little boring and tunnelling creatures set up house in the hull. It rots and it rusts. Decks fall in, beams droop, and the sides fall outward, leaving the stronger-built stem and stern pointing forlornly to a watery sky. A hundred years after she went down, now skeletal and festooned with funeral weed, a ship is still vaguely recognizable. Longer than that, and the semblance begins to disappear completely. The bow and stern finally collapse, the corals plant seed, live, die, and are re-born, coating the wood and iron with an increasingly thick calcareous crust. In time the original ship is buried under their dead skeleton of lime, and all the eye of the diver can discern through his face mask is a series of swollen lumps and bumps which appear much like the rest of the surrounding reef. In fact the ship has become a reef, part of the sea itself, decently buried in Davy Jones's locker.

How, then, do you find a very old wreck? It can sometimes be extremely difficult, even when you have a sound idea of where the ship went down. But after a time you develop an eye for significant signs, like an old miner who, from long practice, notes every pebble and outcrop of rock he passes, unconsciously alert for the signs of a mineral lode. A wreck diver has a similar mental inventory of things to look for in his search. For instance, there are no straight lines in nature, and precious few perfect circles. Squares, angles, unnatural lines or other bottom irregularities out of context with the normal sea-bed are sometimes the first indication of a buried wreck. They are easily missed by the unpractised diver, but as unmistakable as a highway sign in 12-inch lettering if you know what you're looking for. Metals help, too. Brass gives off a vulgar, bright verdigris stain on rocks and surroundings, and coral is reluctant to grow on it. Lead shows snow-white. Iron becomes bulbous and leprous with orange rust and growth, but gives a typical iodine stain to anything growing on it or around it. A combination of these metals causes unnatural piebald coloring and patchy growth on the sea floor which registers at once in the eye of an experienced wreck hunter.

There are also characteristic clues to wrecks of various periods. In the Mediterranean the sites of really ancient wrecks can still be easily discerned because the cargoes of wine, grain and perishables were carried in huge earthenware jars called amphorae. The wrecked vessels are rotted entirely away, but the age-resistant earthenware jars from their holds, some 3000 years old, remain on the bottom, tombstones marking ancient maritime tragedies. We swam on a number of these wrecks off Spain and Sicily, and in the blood-warm water off North Africa. Some of the red pottery carried marks of potters' hands and looked as though it had been made the year before our visit, not some time before Christ. Sailing ships from the 1500's to early 1800's are best identified by the cannon which all of them carried. Usually these are the only easily recognizable things left. Sometimes looking like coral drainpipes on the sea floor—and even these can be hard to spot. I remember the wreck of a ship sunk in 1656 called the *Vergulde Draeck* (*Gilt Dragon*). Her guns and anchors had become fused into the living reef, their outlines obliterated by a garden growth of weeds, anemones and coral. Many divers swam past her blindly, hunting fish, before a fifteen-year-old schoolboy named Graeme Henderson dived into a cave and was startled to find an elephant tusk sticking out of the reef. Since the thought of an elephant swimming from Africa seemed a little preposterous Graeme, his father Jim Henderson, brother Alan, and friends Alan Robinson and John Cowen, hurried back. They found the cannon and anchors near the tusks and, on later dives, pottery and pieces of eight. The *Gilt Dragon* became a famous wreck, though later the partners broke up in bitterness. Another wreck lay unsuspected in the surf off one of Perth's better-known surf beaches at Cottesloe, passed over by thousands of swimmers, surfboard riders and dinghy fishermen. In 1956 a diver named Barry Martin discovered that what everyone for years thought were old sewer pipes were in fact cannon, centuries old. After that, people kept finding drainpipes and insisting they were cannon.

We had feared that the *Batavia*, pummelled constantly by big seas on her exposed shelf of coral, would have been sluiced as bare as a washboard with little remaining except the guns and anchors. We were delighted to find the contrary. The wreck was in an astonishing state of preservation, considering her location in the wash of the surf and 334 years of pounding by the waves.

Over the years the sea had dug a grave for the old ship. It started with the gulley grooved when her keel ran up into the coral with the crash that threw Francisco Pelsaert from his bunk on that June 4th morning before daylight. The sea had enlarged, scoured, and eaten at the edges of the gash until, by the time we arrived, there was hollowed a hole the shape of the ship, 200 feet long, and 12 feet deep. Now the main wash of the waves passed with eddies and swirls and white, confused foam over the tope of the hole, and the skeletal *Batavia* lay partly-protected from the main surges and the storms twenty feet below the surface. In the bottom of this hollow lay the bronze cannon, the spiked, twelve-foot anchors—she had been carrying eight spares in her hold, as well as bow and stern anchors—and wonderful buried things, which we would excavate from beneath the protecting crust of reef which covered what remained of the crushed and flattened hull.

To anyone venturing below the sea for the first time and with us on that day, there may have seemed little to see—no apparent reason for the telltale heavy bubbles and quick, jerky movements which showed unusual excitement and effort among the divers on their first dive on the wreck. From the surface all that could be seen were the guns, some odd square shapes of stone, the anchors, and the contours and convolutions of the reef. There was nothing to suggest a ship or cargo; no high poop or barnacled binnacle, no chests of treasure with pieces of eight spilling onto the sand. Only reef? The divers knew better. After long experience on wrecks they knew what to look for. They could be seen in odd attitudes in the underwater weightlessness standing on their heads, groping in crevices, fins waving against the current and bubbles mounting to the surface. They were digging in sand patches and sending up clouds of shell grit which drifted like smoke in the current . . . tapping gently with the all-purpose tools we used for chipping coral (a hybrid of hammer and pickaxe) . . . occasionally sending the clink of metal on metal echoing across the watery gully. . . . A couple of them were working so far under ledges of reef that only bubbles and the very tips of their fins showed. Peering through misted masks, sucking rubber-tasting air through mouthpieces, they were unconscious of everything save the reef face in front of them. Sometimes they waited patiently for a minute or more for their eyes to become accustomed to the darkness of a cave or crevice.

In the course of my own explorations, swimming along the line of guns jettisoned by the sailors under High Boatswain Jan Evertsz (they were all lying with their muzzles facing north), I saw George Brenzi and Naoom Haimson trying to communicate in diver's sign language. Obviously the message wasn't getting through and their frustration was a little comical. It is impossible to talk underwater, of course, except in grunts; but there is an official international code of hand language with about twenty signs. Divers who often work together develop quite an uncanny understanding of each other. But on this first *Batavia* dive, finger and arm signals were totally inadequate—no superlatives. They tried hard enough. I caught Maurie Hammond, camera in hand, looking like a Martian attempting a hornpipe, and swallowed some salt water laughing at him. He told me later he wanted to show me a particularly beautiful fish that lived under an anchor. His antics frightened it away, and I never did understand down there what he meant. We were down nearly an hour, though it seemed to me only a few minutes from the time we had plunged overboard until I felt my breathing become tight. Looking down at the Sea Bee's air gauge, I saw that it was down below the 500-pound danger mark—not many breaths left before the brass pointer would drop to zero.

When I came up beside the boat, unbuckling my quick-release harness with a quick flip as my head broke the surface, George Brenzi was already aboard. He leaned over to take my fourteen-pound lead belt and forty-pound aqualung—suddenly heavy out of the neutral buoyancy of the sea—and shouted something.

"What's that?" I said, slightly deaf from the change of pressure on my eardrums and the tight-fitting hood of the wet suit.

"Fabulous . . . !"

"You can say that again."

We grinned hugely at each other as I hauled myself over the gunwale, streaming salt water. George passed me a towel as I hooked two thumbs under the chin of the hood and peeled it off with a sucking noise. Another movement opened the jacket front. My skin was warm, almost hot, despite the cold water; the wet suits prevented water circulation and trapped body heat. It was possible to sweat under them and they protected us from coral as well as cold.

"Did you see the keel timbers?" George asked.

"No. Where were they?"

"That ledge at the south end is all wood, with just a light crust of coral over it. There could be all kinds of things jammed up under the woodwork."

I rubbed myself with the towel and told him about the cannon with the crest and the 1616 date and the fish that lived in the barrel. George produced a splinter of blackened oak from the sleeve of his wet suit like a conjurer performing a trick.

"Incredible, isn't it, that woodwork should last three centuries?"

"Well, if the wood has lasted so well, there should be a swag of other stuff down there . . ."

"There is. I could feel all sorts of shapes and angles under the sand when I dug down."

There was a clang on the side and Naoom Haimson dropped his digging tool into the boat. He spat his mouthpiece out and it sputtered and bubbled as he unhitched his lung. We hoisted it aboard and laid it beside the other two metal cylinders forward. He heaved over the side with water running off his black wet suit, looking like a short, sleek seal.

"There's pottery down there." He rubbed his face hard with the towel George passed over. "I cleared a bit of reef," he went on eagerly, spitting some water out, "but I couldn't get them out. Just a row of bottoms. Jugs maybe. Pretty fragile, I'd guess. It should take another hour's work to get them free and we'll have to be very careful or they'll break up."

The others came back in a group; Max Cramer, Greg Allen, Dave Tanner, Maurie with his camera. Rising beside the boat in a foam of bubbles, they passed their lungs up, each one flopping over the stern corner of the aluminium tender and moving forward to make room for the next man. Their smiling faces and eyes belied the typical understatements and flat comments of divers.

"Not a bad sort of a wreck . . ."

"What did you have down in that cave George? A mermaid or a chest of gold? The way you were kickin' up the sand there . . ."

"That forward cannon with the scroll is kind of neat . . ."

(If they'd found a treasure down there, it would have been "not bad" or "kind of neat.")

Merv Brown, the serious one who never made jokes, said: "I think I've got a seventeenth century prefab down below." He took off his rubber hood carefully and smoothed back his moustache.

"A what. . . ?" They looked doubtfully at him.

He put his camera away with care. "Yep. That's right."

"Well, I'm a builder and I didn't see any loose houses below," said Max.

"Did you see that mound of square stones then?" Max nodded. "Well, they're cut sandstone, or something very similar, and if you dig around the edge of the pile, you'll find a couple of fluted colonnades. I'd bet that the whole lot was the façade for an important building in the East Indies and they were shipping it out to Java as ballast aboard the *Batavia.*"

The divers looked impressed. It made sense.

"And when it didn't arrive," Merv continued, "it's possible that they sent a repeat order and ordered a new one exactly the same from Holland—probably they didn't have the kind of stone they wanted in

Java. The building may still be standing somewhere in the old colonial section of Jakarta that used to be Batavia before President Sukarno bundled the Dutch out and changed the name of the place." He smiled at us, pleased with the notion of a white-fronted old colonial building gently decaying among the canal scents, Merdeka slogans and brown faces of modern Jakarta. It was an entertaining thought.

The boat tossed and jerked at her anchor rope. The swells rolled under us, humped, flung back their heads, and broke across the reef in muted thunder and gurgling foam. We sat in our rubber suits and talked about the wreck and the things we had seen, putting together a composite picture from our experiences. The divers' eyes shone, and they talked with affected nonchalance . . . It was a magnificent wreck. We could see the Navy divers over on Dave's boat and the Army men perched in their Zodiac rubber dinghy, talking and moving their arms, but the surf drowned out what they were saying. It seemed to amuse Dave, who leaned in the stern, his green oilcloth-peaked cap pulled down over his eyes.

It was a long time before someone looked at a watch and then quickly up at the sun dropping low toward Evening Reef. "Crikey. We'd better get going."

We were tired by the time we had unloaded the boats and pulled them up the coral beach where the mutineers had dragged their flat-bottomed island-built skiffs. Lungs were lined ready for recharging, wet suits hung out to dry over Beacon Island thornbushes, and weary feet dragged up the coral path. The sun became an orange ball, swelled into a golden basket, distended sideways into an ellipse, and dropped suddenly under the rim of the sea, leaving little gold-flecked clouds overhead and a black ocean below.

Maurie Hammond, with a glass of beer in one hand and a long spoon in the other, cooked spaghetti for us all that night in a huge cauldron. It was his special dish and Italy never saw spaghetti bolognese cooked the way Maurie did it, with square of steak, garlic, tomatoes, and a half-gallon bottle of Marsala wine. The kitchen windows steamed up and good food odors and conversation floated around the room over the white pine table. The five-room shack was roughly built and unpainted and owed nothing to formal architecture, but it was snug against the piercing winds of the Abrolhos; a warm, kindly refuge for a fisherman after a day on the ocean or for divers who had been working below it. We wolfed the meal, hungry as only men who have been on the sea can be. It was one of Maurie's most endearing traits that he liked nothing better than to cook over a hot stove for a bunch of grumbling divers who would eat enough to burst a horse, mop their plates with bread, and say accusingly, "Is that *all?*" Maurie's answer was to growl back at them with mock ferocity, then produce more potatoes, bread or stew.

We were drowsy and comfortable after the evening meal, limbs aching with pleasant fatigue, and were reluctant to go out into the cold night wind that was already whipping little whitecaps off the shallows. But we had to go to the GPV, anchored a mile off, to confer with Hec Donohue and the Navy men about the next day's work on the wreck. There was much to talk over. The wreck had to be surveyed, mapped and photographed; the bronze guns had to be lifted, the relics excavated; and we also had to examine the islands, and dig in the likely-looking spots. There was rather less than a fortnight in which to do all this; after that we ran out of leave, stores, and money. Our biggest worry was the weather. In all our planning we had prayed for the few fine days we would need for cannon-lifting and photography . . . days with no southerly busters, deep depressions forming out in the Indian Ocean, or dropping barometers.

We had decided beforehand that the Navy and Army divers deployed under Lieutenant Donohue would map the wreck and lift the gun aboard the GPV. The Navy had already built a raft of twenty or so 44-gallon oil drums lashed together with a torpedo gantry perched rakishly atop to lift the cannon, and it had been freighted to the islands by the Army boat. The civilians, who had all worked on a number of wrecks before and knew their special jobs thoroughly, were to do the actual archaeological work and the photography. This was the oyerall plan. In practice we shared forces when necessary and helped wherever men were needed most. Army divers chippd away carefully at pottery, Navy men poked under ledges and Merv Brown probably did more than any other single man on the cannon-raising. The mapping was to be done by laying a grid of ropes with fathom markings across the wreck area and taking underwater compass bearings, transcribed initially and roughly on a slate by Lieutenant Donohue, who would later transfer them to a more formal map. Donohue was a slight, dark-haired young man with very blue eyes and an Irish sense of humor, a terror in bars and night clubs off-duty, in a certain Navy tradition. On the job he was a dedicated diving officer. And he was very serious about the *Batavia.*

The lifting of the cannon was to be accomplished, we planned, by looping wire slings around a gun and making the slings fast to the hook of a chain suspended from the raft's winch. Two beefy Navy men, Pappy Gault and Maurie Giles, would then heave on the winch until the chain or their hearts or something gave—or the cannon broke free of the bottom. Dave Johnson would then tow raft-cannon-and-all in a cloud of exhaust fumes and splutter to a spot in quiet water well away from the reef. There the Navy GPV would be able to lift the three tons of dripping sea-greened old metal on her derrick and transfer it to her hold. Fine. Splendid. Simple—so easily set down on paper before the expedition began. But in fact the cannon-raising was to be frightening, easily the most perilous and hair-raising operation of the entire expedition.

Risks were one of the things we talked about. They were an accepted part of diving, and it was useless to pretend they didn't exist. Under water, man is out of his natural element, vulnerable. We were proud of the fact that in the past we had brought our divers back alive from expeditions; but it was partly because we considered the risks carefully and guarded against them. Any of a number of things could kill one of our divers. Sharks? A distant possibility. There were plenty about in Abrolhos waters, skulking in from the 27-fathom deeps: whalers with their high tail fins, mean yellow eyes and treacherous dispositions . . . tiger sharks with square heads, heavy bellies and insatiable appetites . . . hammerheads with ghastly gargoyle countenances . . . Most fearsome of all were the Carcharodon, the Great White Sharks, sometimes with reason called the White Death—the only shark which has no fear and has regularly attacked divers. They were sea wolves all, appearing swiftly and silently out of the depths, sometimes in packs, circling, watching, waiting . . . sleek-skinned, smooth-swimming. Beautiful bastards. Divers have died after attacks by sharks in Australian waters, but it was a rare enough occurrence and we had no particular fear of them on the *Batavia* expedition, though we would take the normal precautions.

Generally speaking, sharks hunt at night, and our work would be accomplished during the daytime. There was a matter of psychology, too. We were unfamiliar creatures and they would be wary of us—

sharks are cautious. Some of us had killed sharks with spearguns, for the heart-thumping thrill of tackling something large and dangerous. Though sharks have an extraordinary tenacity for life and will writhe and snap and attack even though almost cut in half or disemboweled, they have a vulnerable spot—the brain and nerve center, located in the pointed nose just forward of the eyes. If you can hit this, even in a very big shark, it will almost certainly kill him. The danger is in missing. A wounded or ineffectually-hit shark may become a berserk killer. So shooting sharks is rather like shooting elephants; you must wait until the last possible second before pulling the trigger to be sure that the spear thuds home into the vital area, which is a little larger than a small saucer. Recently, explosive heads have made the job much easier, expanding the target from something like three inches in diameter to virtually anywhere in the head. We considered them a little unsporting —if you can be unsporting with a shark. We were all aware, from the sharpness of the razor jaws mounted as trophies on our walls at home, that even a small shark could kill a diver with ease if he went about it in a really determined way. The bite is almost always in the back of the leg, cutting the femoral artery; death results quickly from shock and loss of blood. But sharks, like the hydrogen bomb, could be lived with, providing you observed the rules. Sharks would only trouble us if they took us so much by surprise we did not see them—in murky water, for instance, or if we were injured or swimming on the surface. Only sick fish swim on the surface. Divers in shark water never swim on the surface if they can avoid doing so; it invites attention.

A greater risk on the *Batavia* expedition would be waves. On the edge of the reef the swells ran in regularly, much the same size and shape most of the time. But every so often, perhaps once in an hour, there would be a number of much bigger waves, often running in sets of three. And particularly on windless days there would sometimes come without warning or apparent reason a wave so much bigger than all the others that it would dwarf them into insignificance, breaking with a thundering crest, roaring and crashing on the reef. It is these freak waves, caused when two or sometimes three swells run together far out in the ocean, which are dangerous. The fishermen know them well, but sometimes even they are caught by them and their boats smashed. Most of the year the waves were so big on the reef that it would have been impossible to dive on the *Batavia*. Even now in the period of calms we could expect some big waves. How would we fare on the bottom? Our divers would be safe, we decided, so long as they were in the gulley of the wreck. It was when they surfaced, perhaps exhausted and with an empty air cylinder, that they were in danger. A great wave might crush them on the reef or sweep them away on the fast-running tide. Extreme caution would be necessary when surfacing. It would be dangerous for the boats, too, and the raft, and we resolved to exercise every care.

Of course we knew that the greatest killer in diving was the human element: carelessness, lack of judgment and, especially, overconfidence. Too much familiarity and neglect of the usual precautions can catch even experienced divers, especially with things like failing to check breathing valves, gauges, or the quick-release buckles on harnesses and lead belts. The two occasions on which I myself have come really close to drowning with breathing equipment have both occurred because of things which were so apparently unimportant, I didn't even consider them. When the emergency came it was unexpected and I almost didn't make it back to the top. Surviving, I became doubly cautious.

There are three trite but significant sayings in underwater work: "There are old divers and bold divers; but no old-bold divers"; "It's the little things that kill you"; "After seven minutes without air, you're dead." Scarcely a pleasant subject, but it is only the awareness of the risks and constant safeguarding against them that permits man to enter a world nature never intended him to; allows him to enter the world of the fish—and come back.

It was what allowed us to dive on the *Batavia* wreck.

19 . THE COINS GLINTED WITH OLD WORLD SILVER

Coins were objects of speculation and interest from the beginning. Everyone knew about the chest of 8000 rix-dollars Pelsaert had left on the wreck, supposedly jammed by a cannon and an anchor. But though we all swam watchfully around every anchor and peered under each scrolled cannon butt, no loot was in evidence on the first dive.

"I turned over every rock on the whole damn wreck," said Naoom Haimson.

"I wouldn't be too optimistic about the coins," I said lightly. "The chest has probably broken up and all the doubloons washed away."

They glared at me. Hell, a treasure *was* a treasure. We had gone over all the notes and Henrietta's articles very carefully, that night. Particular attention was paid to a passage, originally penned by Francisco Pelsaert as an entry in his log on this very island. It was written in precise script, perhaps with a seagull quill, 334 years before . . .

October 12 . . . Before noon the weather was somewhat calmer and the Sea being smooth I have gone with the divers to the Wreck; they dived up 75 reals in loose money which had fallen out of a chest; and at last they found still another chest with Money upon which lay a piece of Cannon which, through a sudden wind and the smallness of the little yawl we had to leave with heart's regret.

They intended to raise it later, but were unable to locate it again; in the meantime their big sloop with its crew of *Sardam* skipper Jacob Jacobsz and three sailors was lost in a squall and never seen again. They sailed without the chest, Pelsaert writing apologetically in his journals that by November 12, divers had returned from a last trip to the wreck, "Declaring upon their Manly Truth that nothing more could be found even if one remains lying here indefinitely."

The Dutch in Batavia did not forget their lost silver so easily. When van Diemen—the same Councillor Antonie who had been critical of Pelsaert, now risen to Governor—sent Abel Tasman with three ships on a second voyage to explore the Australian coast, following his brilliant exploration to the south of the continent and New Zealand in 1642, van Diemen ordered the navigator to:

> . . . Further continue your course along the Land of d'Eendracht [Australia] as far as Houtman's Abrolhos, and come to anchor there at the most convenient place, in order to make efforts to bring up from the bottom the chest with eight thousand Rix dollars sunk from the lost ship Batavia in 1629 owing to a brass half-cannon having fallen upon it, and which the men of the yacht Sardam dived for without success, and so save the same together with the said gun which would be a good service done to the said Company. . .

Tasman never sighted the low, gray islands of the Abrolhos.

Pelsaert's chest remained fathoms deep with the *Batavia* wreck. His divers had not been disgraced in leaving it. The four Indians from Gujarat and the two Hollanders (the Indians were probably pearlers, but it is strange that white men should have been diving in that century) had swum down three fathoms, holding their breath, peering about them with unprotected eyes, half-blind in the blur of the water. They had dived till their lungs ached, their heads buzzed, and their eyes were red-rimmed and weeping from the salt. And—for the Honorable Company—from that shambles of splintered wood, twisted cables and snaring ropes that was the wreck, they recovered ten of the twelve money chests, a quantity of silver dishes and candlesticks, carpenter's chests, chests of tinsel and loose coins, all at some peril to their lives. One hopes that the Company was suitably grateful.

Our men, without wishing the shades of their predecessors any harm, were profane about their efforts. "They could have left three or four chests to make things interesting," grumbled Maurie Hammond. Still, even one chest—plus the loose coin from the chest which the French soldier Jean Thirou had broken open during the plundering on board after the wreck—was something. There were some bets placed about who would find the coins. "I'll bet anyone a quid I find the first silver coin," said George in a sleepy voice as we were climbing into our sleeping bags after returning from the Navy boat.

The next day when we were resting after a dive, sitting in the de Havilland boat, bucking at anchor just beyond the surf line, we thought George was joking when he broke the surface, spat out his mouthpiece and shouted, "I've found the loot!" But a minute later he reached the boat with powerful strokes and tossed something over the side that landed with a heavy metallic clunk. It looked like a big green biscuit and we knocked our heads together trying to look closer. George swung dripping over the gunwhale after it and pounced with a hairy paw. Scratch, scratch, scratch went the blade of his diving knife, as he levered impatiently at the emerald crust and we breathed hotly over his shoulder. The encrustation yielded reluctantly until we could see the head of a bearded man and a blurred inscription. The knife point slipped and the score-mark gleamed bright with Old World silver.

"Aha!" George chuckled triumphantly.

"Pieces of eight!" shrieked Maurie Hammond, sounding like Long John Silver's parrot. Grabbing his aqualung, he somersaulted backward over the side with a heavy splash.

George uncovered a date with the point of his knife. "Here—look; 1626, with the '2' shaped like a 'z'," he said.

There were more splashes.

"Are there any more down there like that?" I asked eagerly. "Hey! Wait for me!" The boat was empty.

I had a quick glimpse of George disappearing below the surface like a black, sounding whale. The others had scrambled into the water so fast, some of them had taken paint off the side of the boat with their cylinders. I grabbed mask and flippers, dragged them on hastily and struck the water myself in the usual entry confusion of foam and bubbles. Shoulder-rolling in the weightlessness over and downward, I followed the trail of air bubbles left by the others on their 45-degree dive from the mirror-surface above, swallowing hard to clear the increased pressure on my eardrums and blowing some unwanted water out of my mask.

I found them, Sea Bee air cylinders bracketed to their backs, flippers waving rythmically to balance against the current swirl, drifting around peering under racks. They reminded me of an office staff on hands and knees, looking under desks for a lost two-shilling piece. George beckoned and winked through his mask. The coins were underneath a big boulder, stuck to the rocks. Sections of green circles and ovals showed through the sand drift. We moved our hands to swirl away the sand, obscuring our view momentarily with the particles in suspension. When the miniature sandstorm had been cleared by the current, we saw more of the green biscuits. Significantly there were no cannon nearby. It seemed that these may have been loose coin from the box smashed open by the mutineers . . . "and at last in Drunkenness have thrown them at each others' heads . . ." They had been scattered and trapped in hollows on the bottom, and through the years chemical action by the salt water had formed a corrosive encrustation which had welded them tightly to the coral. They didn't look like coins in this condition and would have meant little to a casual observer; but Brenzi, a veteran of many wrecks, had recognized them as soon as he caught sight of the telltale, unnatural green in the sand under a large lump of coral. "Once you've seen them you can't mistake them," he had said. He was an old hand at coin-seeking from the *Gilt Dragon* wreck. It was an art to free them from the reef without breaking them, because some were worn thin and brittle by water and sand action. They stuck tight; so tight that some broke in half when pried off, or left sections of themselves and their inscriptions on the stone. We found the best method of removing them undamaged was to use a screwdriver as a chisel, tapping the point into the reef slightly below the coin so that it came away with a piece of reef attached. The clinging, dead coral limestone didn't matter; careful acid treatment would remove that later.

The coins were thick-edged and wonderfully heavy in the hand—ninety-four percent silver. Unlike modern money, made of cheaper alloys and in comparison light enough to blow away in a strong gust of wind, each or any of these heavy coins could have been used as a paperweight. We brought about twenty of them back to the boat. The divers turned them over lovingly in their hands, fingering the inscriptions. They were big—big enough so that your encircling forefinger and thumb would only go part of the way around their rims.

"Real spending money," said Max. "Rather satisfying, don't you think, to be able to rattle one of these down on a bar counter so that it rang like a church bell and shout at the barkeeper, 'Forsooth, a flagon, ye knock-kneed knave!' "

Maurie Hammond photographed us with the silver discs in our hands, roughly cleansed with knife blades and rubbing.

The first date we found was 1626, but later ones dated back to 1609, and some were to be as early as 1575. They carried the names and faces of obscure European royalty and national inscriptions. We argued about where they had been minted.

"Dutch ducatons and German talers," said Chris Halls the museum man when he arrived later and we passed them over to him.

"German—shouldn't they all be rix-dollars?" queried Merv Brown in disappointed tones.

"Rix-dollars is another name for them," said Chris, with his thick eyebrows bunched together in concentration. "They circulated all over Europe, and Holland used a good deal of German money, as well as Spanish. There was a standard size and weight—a piece of eight in Spanish money, a crown in England, a taler in Germany, a dollar or ducaton in the Netherlands. Dollar is a corruption of the name taler . . . t-a-a-l-e-r. These particular coins were minted by European city-states and princedoms such as Brunswick, and because they usually had a prince's head on one side, were called royal dollars or rix-dollars.

The first coin I found, and one which I retained as a memento, bore the head of a beefy, well-fed gentleman wtih a pompous expression, a ruff, an armor breastplate and a portentous pot belly. "Christian, By the Grace of God Duke of Brunswick and Lunenburg . . . Deus Gratia" proclaimed the Latin inscription. On the reverse side was the ducal arms, a conglomeration of crossed swords, screaming eagles, holly and rampant lions. The date was 1624. Christian had been a leader of mercenaries during the Thirty Years War which devastated 17th century Germany—onc of the cruellest and most prolonged conflicts in history. The armies of the various German, Swedish, Danish and Austrian princes lived off the unfortunate populace, killing, raping and stealing as they went along. In this conspicuously unpleasant company, Christian distinguished himself. His epitaph in history is: "A plunderer of peasants as well as priests . . . One of the most brutal Condottiere of the war, and a foul-mouthed censor of would-be peacemakers." Christian lived and died by the sword. Wounded on the battlefield in 1626, he lost an arm, and died sick and defeated soon after. Three years later this coin, stamped with his brutal features, has come 10,000 miles to sink on a coral reef off a continent Christian had never heard of, and grow green over the centuries at the bottom of the sea.

We returned at lunchtime with the coins, elated. For once the divers forgot their studied reserve and showed their excitement: "The rest of the chest shouldn't be far away . . ." But the afternoon had been reserved by plan for cannon-raising. The weather continued to be beautiful—almost a flat calm—and the Navy had been working all morning with bolts and spanners, getting the raft ready. We gobbled our lunch. "You lot!" said Petra with a gesture of mock despair. "You'll give yourselves indigestion, truly." She gave us one of her warm smiles and shook her head as the last diver scurried out anxiously with a piece of bread and jam in his hand and the door banging behind him.

We knew the weather, and we mistrusted it. "It's too good to be true," Max Cramer kept saying. We all felt the tense urgency to dive and dive while it lasted. Dave Johnson's boat was already well down the channel, towing the cannon-raising raft of drums with the torpedo gantry on top, when we returned.

The cannon-lifting went well, in a tight-nerved fashion. Dave Johnson towed the cumbersome raft around by the deep channel, with a pall of exhaust smoke and heat fumes rising behind G70. The sea was so calm it was miraculous. They had selected the Long Tom, a rakish cannon near the bow, as the lightest and easiest cannon to lift first. In the slight swell, Merv Brown and Petty Officer "Smiley" Asher, a square, blond Navy man who was Hec's boss diver, went down and fixed the wire loops around the gun. A school of buffalo bream milled around, blotting out the men below in their desperate curiosity to see what in Neptune's name these strange creatures from the world above were doing now. A dark rockfish, called a "Jack Johnson" because of its pugnacious expression, appeared indignantly at the mouth of his home in the cannon barrel. There seemed to be one resident fish in every gun.

"Heave away!"

The men on the raft pulled obediently on the endless chain. The slings tightened until it seemed they must snap. Divers' heads appeared anxiously on the surface. "Nothing's happening!" they said, and bobbed below again. The raft hands groaned on the winch. The cannon refused to budge. Then a slight swell rolled through, shouldering under the raft, exerting tremendous pressures. There was a cracking and creaking underwater, and suddenly in a cloud of coral dust the cannon burst free from its bonds of three centuries. Fish and divers started and scattered like sparrows as the cannon began to swing like a berserk battering ram below the raft, knocking off corners of reef, threatening to crash into other cannon, lurching uncontrollably. . . . "For God's sake get it into deep water before it smashes everything!"

the divers shrieked in an agony of apprehension, heads popping through the surface like champagne corks. Dave couldn't hear them above the motors, but he could see the urgency in their faces, and eased the boat into gear. At first the water just frothed behind the stern; but gradually the roaring, buzzing 40-hp Evinrude outboard and the chuffing diesel straining in weird tandem began to make an impression.

The boat drew away from the reef. The hands on the raft and the divers in the water cheered and waved exultantly. Suddenly everyone felt very warm and very good. On the bottom we watched the cannon as it passed overhead, still swinging menacingly, suspended below the raft. The cannon-raisers swam past in escort, gave us the thumbs-up sign of triumph, and glided with it out of sight, followed by schools of curious fish. I noticed one little fish suddenly lonely and bewildered. It was the Jack Johnson which had lived in the cannon barrel, his whole world upside-down in catastrophe. I felt sorry for him, but he looked so comical in his dismay that I couldn't help laughing at him.

We carried on with our excavations. Under a jutting coral ledge we found more woodwork. Further digging with gloved hands, pick-axes and crowbars showed that ribs and planking were buried under the reef; and still more excavation revealed a substantial section of ship and the glint of brasswork. The brass proved to be a two-and-a-half-foot, roughly-made canister of curious shape with a base about eight inches across. It looked like a giant bushman's quart pot. In the boat, scraping out the inside brought forth the distinctive and acrid reek of gunpowder. The object was a powder measure for the big cannon. Continued burrowing into the reef disclosed more of them, and cannon balls so soft and porous after years below the sea that they were like black, pasty carbon.

Naoom waved a gloved hand and blew some excited bubbles. He had at last uncovered a corner of his pottery. We worked around it with delicate care, nervous in case we should break it, or lest the object should be already broken or incomplete. But after a half hour of patient levering and picking at the reef, he worked loose a perfect jug. Max found two more in another section of the wreck. They were almost identical; each was round, with ornate crests stamped into its brown earthenware belly and a single handle joined to the neck. What we at first thought was coral warting turned out to be a man's face engraved on the side of the neck . . . a stern face, making the jug look like a comical, pompous old man with a Falstaffian belly, turned-down mouth and permanently-soured disposition. Curious . . . It was not until later that we found that it was a Bellarmine jug. They were common at the time of the *Batavia* and there was something of a story behind them.

The face on the jugs was a caricature of Robert Cardinal Bellarmine (1542–1621), whose anti-Protestant activities in Holland in the early 1600's during the religious troubles made him so unpopular that his anti-Papist opponents conceived this method of lampooning him. They stamped his face on alehouse jugs, and it caught on—no matter how the fat cardinal fumed. Within a short time Bellarmine jugs were standard in public houses from the Rhine to England. For convenience they came in several sizes: gallonier, four-pint, quart, and pint. Every time a customer took a drink he laughed at Cardinal Bellarmine. Among the famous men who swigged merrily from the necks of Bellarmines brimming with foaming ale were William Shakespeare and Ben Jonson. The jugs also had another use which in later years earned them the title "witch bottles." They are still occasionally found buried under hearths or thresholds of old houses in England with cloth figures, twists of human hair, nail parings, and other personal items. In some cases they were intended to ward off evil spirits and protect against witchcraft; others had a more sinister purpose. When the cloth figures were pierced with pins and bizarre ingredients like frog's livers and bat's claws were included, the purpose was to cast an evil spell on somebody—put a hex on them. Bellarmines enjoyed about fifty years of use before fashions changed and the stoneware factories in Germany, Flanders and Fulham (England) turned to other styles. By that time, of course, Cardinal Bellarmine had been dead and buried many years, the Protestant Reformation was well established in Holland and the Low Countries, and the original purpose of the jugs was forgotten. Now here was old Cardinal Bellarmine glowering at us from the neck of a jug off the wild Australian coast. The last man to drink from the jug had been perhaps a bearded Dutchman of the *Batavia* mutiny, with scurvy-gapped teeth and a cutlass at his belt.

By the end of the third day of diving, everyone was smiling but Maurie Hammond. He was sad because we had shifted two cannon and he would have liked more time to photograph them from different angles, to catch the little striped fish fluttering about them in his lenses, to experiment with light and color in a thousand frames. But we had to harden our hearts. The weather was perfect for photography, but it was also ideal for lifting the guns. We watched the horizon nervously for signs of a change, gave Maurie as much time as we could, and in the end moved the guns. Our excavations produced some astonishing things. We found the calibrated rim from a celestial globe, a navigator's protractor, and a pair of mapping dividers which intrigued Hec Donohue when he saw them.

"They're just like my own pair," he said. "A bit of spit and polish and you could navigate around the world with 'em."

"I hope you'd do a better job than the last bloke who used them—Ariaen Jacobsz," said Max. We also hauled up some sounding leads, much the same as those still in use today; some long pipelike objects which we thought might be culverin barrels; and some pretty blue-and-white pottery lamps. The most interesting find was an object which Max dug out from a mass of pitch and gunpowder sealed below the reef. It was brass and for a while he was convinced he had found the ship's bell. It proved to be a chemist's mortar, with a heavy relief around its rim and the Latin inscription AMOR VINCIT OMNIA—love conquers all. Had it belonged to Cornelisz, the only known apothecary aboard. . . ? A strange motto for that strange man, but perhaps within the scope of his twisted philosophy.

Once, after Naoom Haimson had worked a little brown earthenware jug out of the reef like a loose tooth, my heart flew into my mouth at the sight of the silver rows of coins. Pelsaert's chest! No such luck. It was someone's private hoard, left in the panic of the shipwreck; about fifty rix-dollars, with dates going back to 1575, and a rich variety of other coins. They were probably worth a small fortune in those days; their owner must have had many heart-searchings about leaving them.

We displayed the coins, jugs, powder canisters, navigation instruments and the chemist's mortar rather proudly on the kitchen table that evening for the Navy and Army men who had come in after completing their mapping (we had been tangling in their ropes and shaking fists at each other all day). They were impressed. Hec whistled. "Wait till Henrietta sees this lot!"

——which reminded me with a start that she was due the next day.

20 | HENRIETTA AND OTHER DISCOVERIES

Paradoxically Henrietta's reaction was not one of instant pleasure when the discovery of the wreck was first announced.

"You wretched boys!" she said.

"But it's where you said it was—or near enough," I said in some surprise.

"Yes, but I wish you'd found it earlier."

She had just finished her book, *Voyage to Disaster*. It had passed through proofreading stages, was set up and ready for printing and release in a matter of weeks and it contained a chapter arguing Goss Island as Batavia's Graveyard and Noon Reef as the site of the wreck. It now turned out that Beacon Island and Morning Reef were the correct locations.

"Simply infuriating!" said Henrietta, banging her palms together in exasperation. As early as 1952 she had drawn a map suggesting Beacon Island and Morning reef, but had changed her mind when the fishermen told her that there was no beach on Beacon—and Batavia's Graveyard *had* to have a beach because of the evidence of the Predikant's letter about pulling up the little boats. I didn't dare mention that we had said in 1960 that Beacon had a strand of sorts. It really would have been unfair. Henrietta had been right in the basis of her hypothesis about the Wallabis, and it was due to her aggressive championing of these islands as the *Batavia* story site that the wreck had been discovered. Her concern was in part with the extra work now needed to correct the book—rewriting chapters and revising the index—and the upsetting of publication dates. But mostly I suspected it was human irritation at having made a wrong guess.

I pointed out mildly that it was really a blessing; better for the discovery to be made while the book could be corrected. And surely, I said, the excitement and publicity over the wreck, for any book about the *Batavia,* was really rather fortuitous. She looked at me with a jaundiced eye. "I still wish you'd found it earlier. My nerves are frayed. I swear this book has taken ten years off my life."

Henrietta's book was a most competent piece of historical research. It contained a complete copy of Pelsaert's Abrolhos log, including (in horrific detail) the trial records of Cornelisz and the mutineers, and a good deal of invaluable background material.

I balanced my teacup and spoke boldly.

"About the page proofs of your book . . . particularly that section of Pelsaert's log . . . Do you think we could borrow it for our expedition? It would be enormously helpful." (It was still the only complete English translation in existence.)

"Yes," she replied with asperity. "I'm bringing it with me."

"Er. . . ?" I said, taken aback.

"Yes, you naughty boy. You promised me in 1960 that if you ever found the wreck I could come along and see it."

I had, at that.

Mentally I boggled. Henrietta was fine. But hang it all, she was more than sixty years old (though she didn't look it) and had seven grandchildren. The islands were a pretty tough place. What if she should become femininely frail, or fall ill or have an accident? Besides, facilities were pretty primitive. And we were inclined to drop an occasional oath around the bivouac. The work was serious and demanded absolute concentration. It wasn't really a place for women, old or young. So I believed.

"There aren't any b-baths," I said weakly, embarrassed. "The wind blows all the time . . . We'll mostly be out at sea."

She saw through me at once, and fixed me with a look.

"Nonsense. I spent the first five years of my married life living in tents with Geoffrey in the North West frontier country. I love roughing it, and now that the wreck has been found, wild horses wouldn't keep me away. I'll even bring a mask and flippers."

I had no resistance. It was true that I had made the promise in a rash moment—and she had done so much work on the wreck story that she deserved to be included in the hour of triumph. But I was scarcely enthusiastic.

At the time I thought her remark about the mask and flippers was meant as a joke. If I'd known what she really intended, it would have been very detrimental to my peace of mind.

In the absorption of the things we were dredging up from the wreck and the dedication of the diving work, I had almost forgotten Henrietta was coming at all—until Hec Donohue reminded me of it, and Petra Johnson began fussing around the shack in a womanly way, organizing some little feminine touches.

"Do you think she'll like it?" she asked anxiously. She had put bright curtains up, and supplied a bedspread, and a vase of daisies... Petra was a dear.

"Of course she will," we said.

They arrived on a beautiful afternoon. The Army boat under Lieutenant Caskey had made a run to Geraldton for stores and water and picked up Henrietta, Chris Halls, Dick Drok and Jack Sue. Dick, able to stay only a few hours, was happy to be able to see at last, even if only for a short time, the island which had become so real to him in his translation of Pelsaert's journal. The sun was so bright that day and the water so clear that as the *Lerida* came in to the anchorage you could see the blue corals on the bottom in sixty feet of water.

Henrietta, in brown suede jacket and green scarf, was waving gaily from the lee rail. My heart turned to stone when I saw what she had in her hand. "I've brought my mask and flippers!" she called across the water.

I shut my eyes. She'd get drowned, nothing surer, and it would be blamed on me. In my imagination I heard the familiar voice of Perth City Coroner Pat Rodriguez saying sternly: "I am utterly astonished, Edwards, that you should have permitted an elderly woman to enter the water at a place you yourself have described as notoriously perilous..." Dammit, I'd be lucky if I escaped a manslaughter charge.

"Really, it's much too rough," I laughed unconvincingly, lifting her case into the de Havilland aluminium boat. "There's a huge surf all the time . . . far too dangerous . . . show you the photographs later . . ."

She wrinkled her nose as we drove ashore. "It doesn't seem very rough to me."

It was the third day with the early wind dying to a perfect calm, with a white lace of foam on the reef and the sea flat as a billiard table. I could have dunked my six-month-old Christopher in it without danger. But that wasn't the point. With weather like this, we should be working flat-out on the wreck. I didn't want my divers wasting time rescuing Henrietta from a watery grave. And if anything did happen to her—ye gods!

"Well, it may not *look* rough, but I can assure you that quite honestly it's out of the question for you to dive out there."

Henrietta was much too clever for me. She concentrated on David Johnson, charming him with smiles and compliments. By teatime it was obvious that she was going to win her way. She took charge of the camp. Petra was thrilled to have another woman in the shack, and Henrietta, after all the years of dreaming and writing about the *Batavia*—why, here she was on the very spot where it had all happened. She sparkled like champagne, positively glowed in her exuberance, marching briskly from one end of the island to the other and back again in stout walking shoes, the translation of Pelsaert's journal gripped in her hand. Every now and then she stopped to add comments in flourishing rhetoric with dramatic gestures or read from the proofs of *Voyage to Disaster*. She had a simply splendid time and wore out several of the divers who tried to keep up with her.

"Fair dinkum—she knows so much about it you'd think she emigrated on the *Batavia* herself," said one of the soldiers in awe.

Henrietta rapidly established herself as the Duchess of Beacon Island. After dinner she read long extracts from the Journal while we argued and theorized about which islands were Seal's and Traitor's in relation to Beacon Island as Batavia's Graveyard. Now and again she fixed me with a careful look, but she said nothing more about diving, and I began—quite unreasonably—to hope that she had forgotten the idea.

I should have known better, I thought sourly when I came down to the jetty the next morning and found her firmly ensconced in Dave Johnson's boat with some fins in her hand and a Stop-me-I-dare-you expression on her face. I shrugged. I'd done my best. She was on Dave's boat, she was *his* responsibility. Doubtless we'd have to drag her half-drowned out of the water and she would learn her lesson that way. And she would probably be seasick and miserable.

Henrietta, sensing the rather antagonistic mood of the divers on the way out to the wreck, spoke only once. "I wish you'd stop treating me like an old lady. I can assure you that I'm not a fraction as fragile as you silly boys seem to think." Their expressions remained unconvinced and surly. Male prejudice.

Of course she was a magnificent success. Granted that it was the calmest day of the year, with a mirrorlike shining sea reflecting the cloudless sky in blue mirages and twinkling points of light that hurt the eye . . . hardly a ripple to mark the reef; still she did marvellously well. We started her off with a mask and snorkel, a couple of the divers watching rather sardonically. Their expressions changed when she paddled around above the wreck as though she had been snorkeling all her life. It took some people days to learn, and she had mastered it right off. Not bad for an old doll.

"She's doing all right," the divers said grudgingly, abandoning their malicious hope that she'd swallow half the ocean and choke. When she put her head up they gave her a little clap and cheer of encouragement. After she had swum around the wreck—Max and I swimming on each side—and she had watched two divers working down below, she asked if she could use breathing equipment.

Max and I looked at each other. She was doing so incredibly much better than expected. Why not? We had a "hookah" running—a small air compressor which pumped air down 100 feet of plastic hose to an aqualung mouthpiece—which we used as an alternative to aqualung cylinders for heavy, air-wasting work. Henrietta took the mouthpiece with her most determined expression and away she bubbled on the end of the hose.

"Well I'll be blowed—she's a natural diver," said George Brenzi.

Though she didn't go all the way to the bottom she was able to inspect the wreck thoroughly. Her greatest moment came when she embraced the huge bow anchor in a hug of delight. With that dive she won everyone's heart. She had established herself as a diving buddy. It was a considerable achievement for one who should have been, at her age, an old lady. But there was nothing old-ladyish about Henrietta.

"You've got to hand it to her," said Max in admiration.

She became one of the gang, and I was glad because really I like her a lot. In retrospect I decided that this was the main reason for my not wanting her to dive. I'd been rather afraid she'd make a fool of herself before the critical eyes of the divers—not reckoning with the immense capabilities of Henrietta.

Strange how quickly one adapts to new places and situations. We had been in the islands less than a week, but already we had so grown into the atmosphere of the place and the pattern of our diving that it seemed as though we had always been there, and it was the outside world which seemed unreal and dreamlike.

We had established a routine. Usually we went to bed early. The seagulls cried and wailed all night in the darkness outside like distressed ghosts . . . EEEeeeeh. And we awoke early. There was always a thin cold wind at dawn in the Abrolhos, a sea-chilled night breeze that gnawed at the kidneys. We would waken to hear it whistling and moaning in the corrugated iron roof . . . lying there in warm sleeping bags wishing for a little more sleep, but prodded by the thorn of the jobs to be done before the diving could begin.

Soon after 6 A.M., before the sun came up, we would walk out with sleep-blurred eyes, towels over our shoulders for morning ablutions, shivering as we felt the shock of the wind outside the door. The sun came up pale and thin behind Morning Reef, and the water slapped on the little beach where the Predikant Bastiaensz once had to pull the mutineers' little boats up . . . "I have been so weak that I could not get up; I had to pull up and push off the little boats in which they navigated; every day it was—What shall we do with that Man?" Poor, hungry Bastiaensz. We filled our aqualungs on the bank where he had sat in his self-pity. We felt the early wind through Navy sweaters, and often could not dive until nearly midday, when the strong gusts of early morning lulled. Pelsaert observed the same thing. "We have found here that the wind . . . generally blew from the South and South South East . . . so that at the wreck it is always adverse and there is continually a hard surf, and one has to observe precisely the moment of Slechte smooth water otherwise one would never have been able to do anything on the wreck . . ." Like Pelsaert's men, we continually watched the wind and that strip of white foam a mile south.

While we waited for the moment of slack water, we had plenty to do. There were boats to bail and refuel, broken equipment to repair, lines to coil, maybe a torn rubber suit to patch, aqualungs to fill, gear to lay out—all so that as soon as the smooth water came we would be ready to take instant advantage of it. Our gear was international. We had Australian-made Sea Bee aqualungs, similar to many U.S., British and French makes, and based on the original design by the great underwater pioneer, Jacques Cousteau, who released us from the claustrophobic dangers of the old bell-helmet ("hard-hat") diving suits. We also had a couple of Healthways and Porpoise sets, and one Seibe Gorman. Tight-fitting neoprene suits protected us against cold and sharp corals. We had the usual masks, fins, snorkels, lead belts, long spearguns against possible predators, digging picks and crowbars we had specially adapted for underwater use, an air compressor for filling the air bottles to 2200 pounds per square inch . . . knives, gloves, floats, lines, tackle . . . Our boats were de Havilland aluminum hulls, picked because they were proof against the sharp fangs of coral, could even stand a roll-over in heavy surf and were light and seaworthy. The outboard motors propelling them were 18-horse Evinrudes, rugged and reliable. The accent on everything was simplicity, reliability, ease of operation and repair. We avoided complicated gear which we could not mend ourselves if it broke, even though Merv Brown worked wonders with his portable repair shop, aided by George.

"What about another cannon?" Dave Johnson suggested.

Dave had direct blue eyes and a spirit so independent he sometimes offended people who genuinely wanted to help him by his brusque refusals of assistance. He had been through a boys' home as a child and had grown tough and wary as such boys often do, retaining a hard, protective shell around him. He had succeeded first as a lead miner and then as a crayfisherman, both through guts and grim, hard work. He had a prickly pride of his own, and "didn't get on' (his own words) with the other families on Beacon Island. It was a pity he preferred his own company because he was an intelligent and likeable fellow when he relaxed enough to let you know him. His wife Petra was an opposite in temperament, all sweetness and light, and very sociable. She mothered Dave in the nicest possible way and was one of the most understanding women I have met. The cannon-raising would have been impossible without Dave and his boat. He towed the clumsy raft, maneuvering his craft so that it placed the raft directly over the cannon to be lifted, risking the breakers during the worrying period while the lifting slings were attached. He then towed raft, cannon and all away to the dumping ground when the divers had done their work below.

Lifting the cannon became increasingly difficult. Though the fine weather of the first three days continued, the sea was beginning to move, indicating that a break in the weather was on the way. The problem was that while the raft had looked an excellent theoretical method of lifting big guns (and it worked perfectly in flat water) in practice it was difficult in the open sea with a swell running. Normally when lifting heavy objects we would sink drums beside them, fasten them with wire cable or chain, and blow the drums up with air from a long hose, until the drums floated off the bottom and lifted their load. The force they exerted was surprising. One 44-gallon drum would lift 400 pounds. (An inflated kit bag could lift a heavy kedge anchor of 80 pounds.) However, with these exceptionally big and heavy cannon, it would have required an excessive number of drums with individual handling of each along the bottom . . . more work and worry. The raft would do it in one single lift, so we hoped. But in the swells of the open ocean the raft changed character. From the lazy, docile creature it was in the calm shallows, it became alive and cantankerous, rolling, bucking and dipping, refusing to go where it was towed, running with the current, changing its mind and heading off on alternate courses with a perverse agility that was frustrating and infuriating.

When it came to the task of slipping the wires from the tethered cannons below over the hook of the chain suspended from the winch through the center of the raft, the raft became a thing of positive malevolence, even in the tiny waves of this calm day.

Dave Johnson tried to tow the raft into position. It swung and square-bucked away over waves, with the two burly Navy men, Pappy Gault and Maurie Giles, hanging on like cowboys at a rodeo. Down below, the divers risked getting fingers and forearms crushed trying to attach the slings; one minute the cables were slack and drooping, the next they jerked suddenly taut and twanging as banjo strings. The divers were hurled to and fro in the currents, cursing and blowing bubbles of profanity. Finally Leading Seaman Grant Clifford, Dave Reid, Hec Donohue and Merv, and the Army divers Dugdale, Aitken and Urquhart, made all the viciously flicking cables secure below, lashed the chains to prevent their slipping the purchase, and Pappy and Maurie Giles began winding on the winch, soaked by the small waves running over the top of the now anchored raft. It took a long time to break the big cannon out of the coral in a smoking shower of debris, and there were more anxious moments before it cleared the wreck site, Dave towing it in a haze of exhaust smoke and steam to the dumping ground. They moved two more of the leviathans, and each time it became more difficult and dangerous. It had been thought-provoking. . . .

Then there had been the controversy over the explosives. The Navy men were highly trained in explosives and were anxious to try some out on the wreck. But the civilians were divided about the matter. True, the charges might reveal new treasures; but they might also smash fragile glass and pottery and kill off the abundant marine life in the vicinity.

"I think a bit of a bump would do some good," said Hec Donohue longingly, fingering a coil of fuse wire. "Open things up a bit. You might even find that chest," he tried to tempt us.

"It will kill all the fish before I have a decent chance to photograph them," Hammond cried in anguish. "You've no idea what a charge of explosive does to reef life."

"There are plenty more fish in the sea and a charge might crack the coral crust and strip some of the seaweed back so that we can see what's underneath," said George.

"I'm against it," said Max flatly.

I felt some antipathy toward the idea myself—because of the fish—and murmured on those lines.

"I don't know. So long as you're careful . . . It should be all right if you put the charges in the right places," said Merv. He liked the technical problems posed by high explosives.

"Will it kill the crayfish?" Dave Johnson's voice was anxious; they were his livelihood.

"Monstrous blasts and percussions," said Henrietta to no one in particular.

There was a deadlock, but in the end it was pointed out that at least one lot of charges would have to be detonated to break out one of the bronze guns, which was wedged in by half a ton of coral and a piece of iron artillery rusted beyond redemption. The dissenters reluctantly assented to this.

The charges were prepared, taped, checked, fused and laid on the bottom in a tense atmosphere. "No smoking, please," said Hec. A match fizzed, the fuse wire smoked . . . seconds ticked agonizingly away.

"WOOM!!" Water spouted and a pool of black debris boiled up from the bottom.

"Dammit!" said Hec. "Three charges should have gone off."

They had to wait a safe period before going into the water again to reconnect the fuse wire. "Can't see a thing down there—black as pitch," reported the Navy men on their return. George and Merv, used to working with explosives underwater themselves, smiled slightly superior smiles. They had a friendly rivalry with the Navy crew and enjoyed this discomfiture.

But this time there was a gratifying "WOOM! WOOM!"

"All clear," said Hec, mopping his brow.

It was some time before we could dive and when we reached the bottom in a twilight gloom of debris still in suspension, the first tragic sight that met our eyes was dead and dying reef fish. I felt nausea and saw Maurie Hammond wince . . . The sharks would feast tonight. There were so many fish around the wreck that any blast would necessarily have had its casualties. Nevertheless we regretted the slaughter, and would gladly have spared them. In contrast to the mortally injured fish, the crayfish were wobbly-legged, indignant, but alive. They had no hollow cavities in their shelled bodies to be affected by the concussion. Fish with their air bladders, and humans with eardrums and sinuses are most readily affected by underwater blasts.

There were compensations. As the dirt and dust cleared away on the current, we saw a new wreck before our eyes. The blast had stripped the encrustation off several iron cannon, leaving them fresh and clean—though their appearance belied their carbonized nature—and ripped away the weed which had disguised outlines around the wreck. Odd formations we had thought were reef were now revealed as stacks of small bricks—the galley range? . . . the blacksmith's forge? A definite line of woodwork now showed clearly along the keel, with all sorts of inviting nodules and lumps sticking out. A coffee pot and two pewter plates stuck out boldly from the reef, as well as a small jug and more powder canisters. Bits of broken pottery showed losses against the gains. I almost wept over a drinking stein shattered in a thousand pieces. The corner in which Max and I had been making our finds was now outlined much more clearly. We reasoned, from the angle of the wood, the money, lamps and navigation instruments, that it must have been the cabin of an important officer—maybe Ariaen

Jacobsz. Or else it had been a corner of the great cabin and when the ship had sunk, everything had slid along the floor to end up wedged in this section, which later became grown over with reef.

". . . Thump . . . thump . . . thump . . . thump . . ."

Startled, we looked up toward the surface as we were interrupted by a fiendish noise of motors, growing louder and louder. It sounded as though the *Queen Mary* were driving over the top of us. We looked up to see the huge, black bulk and whirling propellors of a big boat, the keel only ten feet over our heads. The GPV? . . . The Navy gone berserk. . . ? We could only hope that no one would get near the propellers as we grabbed our bits of reef hard with both hands to anchor ourselves to the bottom. Divers looked at each other, eyes big and round behind their face masks. The noise receded. Crazy. We shrugged and went on with the work. Later we learned that it was Frank Bombara with the sixty-six foot *Emmalou,* coming in to see what we were about. It was so calm he was able to come right over the wreck. He came back in a dinghy and spent some time bobbing about with a water glass, his grinning face outlined in the circle of glass on the surface. We gave him a rude gesture and beckoned him down, but he shook his head with the emphatic air of a man who was going to keep a boat's keel between him and the bottom at all times. "The only shark that's going to get me is one that can attack through a bath tap," he declared afterward.

Now on the bottom we found even more incredible things: a sailor's leather belt, a knife in a scabbard, fragments of rope and canvas—all preserved in pitch. Divers were busy swimming to and from the boats with their treasures. We grubbed and burrowed into the broken crust of the ship, becoming covered with black paste and gunpowder-smelling sediment, stirring up black clouds of dust loosed by the explosion so that we were in perpetual twilight. When our air gave out we flipped back to the boat and heaved ourselves, exhausted, over the side.

Looking at the finds laid carefully on the deck, Max said, "This does it. With this stuff, the coins, cannons, and navigation instruments, if we didn't find another thing during the rest of the expedition, it would still be a success."

"Thanks to the weather," said George.

"It's been a freak," agreed Maurie Hammond.

We looked gratefully at the blue sea and sky. Hard to believe that on most days of the year waves broke hard and high on the spot where the de Havilland was now rocking gently.

"We've been touched by luck," said Jack Sue.

Almost unconsciously I felt my lucky shark's tooth under my jacket. I saw Maurie Hammond touch wood, and one of the others finger a cross on a chain. Odd how superstitious divers are.

The Army and Navy men came ashore late in the afternoon, fingering the relics and shaking their heads in amazement at the variety of articles that could come out of an apparently barren bit of reef.

Hec Donohue had a message for us. "We'll take the GPV in to Geraldton for fuel and stores over the weekend. Any mail or messages?" As an afterthought he added, "Do you think it would be a neat idea if I took a couple of cannon in with me, to show the world we're making progress?"

Max's face brightened. "They'd be tickled pink in Geraldton."

We would load them in the morning.

But in the morning, for the first time during the expedition, things went wrong. As Maurie Hammond was drifting in the aluminum boat, focusing to photograph the first cannon coming up on the Navy derrick, there was an ominous "CRA-A-A-CK" from the mast.

The cannon had swung over the water, green, coral-encrusted, glorious, streaming with salt water. The winch hands paused anxiously; everyone's attention was riveted on the very top of the wooden mast, where the cracking noise had come from. The iron collar at the top of the mast which took the strain off the pulley blocks had cut halfway through the seasoned timber with the colossal weight of the cannon. Another second and . . .

"Lower away—HURRY, AND LOOK OUT BELOW!" Hec shouted from the bridge. The cannon hurtled back into the sea with a splash as the divers who had attached the slings scuttled out of the way, thrashing the water to foam with their fins to dodge the monster.

There was a moment's silence as ripples from the fall spread across the water. "Phew! That could have been nasty," said Hec.

The cannon had been dropped just in time. If the mast had broken while it was being lowered inboard, the gun's weight would have sent it plummeting straight through the wooden bottom of the ship, sinking her in a few minutes. The falling mast and tackle might well have killed or injured some of the hands on deck.

Hec was ruefully wiping his forehead; Dave Reid, his second-in-command, turned the color of green cheese.

"It was tested in Fremantle," said Pappy Gault, looking angrily up at the mast. It seemed that the cannon was just heavier than anyone had thought.

How had the *Batavia's* gunners handled them, without the benefit of wires or winches? We felt a new respect for the old-time sailors.

"Nothing for it but to get repairs done in Geraldton," said Hec. "The barometer's dropping—the sooner we get going the better."

We waved them good-bye as the GPV belched black smoke, turned her bluff bows southeast and headed for the horizon. Bad-weather clouds, little black puffballs, were dotting the northern horizon. It was time to get the picks and shovels and sieves out to dig in the dry, dusty, historied soil of Beacon Island. The *land* archaeology program.

"Graveyard duties," said George Brenzi.

21 ISLANDS OF ANGRY GHOSTS

George Brenzi and I were slightly pale, wisecracks and repartee gone cold on our lips, as we looked down at the skeleton. It set the little hairs on the napes of our necks prickling. There was something indecently final about it. A skull that once had a tongue to talk, to laugh, to cry out in the pain of its death, now empty, mocking, grinning from the earth at the bad joke of life.

"Not very good-looking is he?" I said slowly to George. "I think I'll be cremated."

George shivered, despite the trickle of sweat running down his forehead, channeling the dust of the digging on his skin.

The skeleton lay full-length on its back, obscenely sprawled, with its head flung back in a hideous grin. There was no mistaking the posture.

"Murdered," George had said with certainty even before we found the sword-chop on the skull.

Wry-faced, we brushed the dust from the bones, while the skull leered up at us with its disarticulated jawbone. Naoom Haimson made an official medical examination, squinting dispassionately through the smoke of his old black pipe. The dead man's injuries were a broken shoulder, a slightly depressed fracture of the skull and a sword chop into the bone; skull and jaw were twisted at an unnatural angle. The man had been running away, been chased by men with cutlasses, chopped down from behind, and his head wrenched back and the throat savagely cut, Naoom said. No one spoke for a minute as we looked into the grave. He had been thrown into the grave like a sack of garbage and his limbs still lay loosely awry, shoulders hunched, as they had when he had been dumped without ceremony into the shallow pit. Beside him the heavy arm bone of another corpse, a companion in death, protruded from the light soil—this body lying under the concrete of the sleeping quarters of Dave's hut.

A year later, while filming a television re-enactment of the expedition with Sydney underwater cameraman Ron Taylor,* I dug under the hut enough to remove the skull of this second man, and found that he too had been done in brutally. The story of his death was told in the three sword chops sunk deep into the bone. The first had caught him at an angle above the left ear from behind, felling him. The second had been an abortive attempt to cut his head off as he groped on the ground, face down. The stroke had missed in the darkness, slicing deep into the back of his head. The third blow had taken off the right point of his jaw from an unusual angle, which at first baffled us in our reconstruction of the crime. Then we reasoned that they had probably finally rolled him over on his back with a callous foot and chopped down to cut his throat, the stroke again slightly inaccurate in the dark, catching his chin. Any one of the blows would have been enough to kill him; there was no need for the second or third. But the mutineers had a lust for killing, and liked the feel of flesh under their blades. Perhaps there had been three men who each delivered a blow. In life, we guessed, he had been a strong man, tall and exceptionally powerful, judging from the thickness of his arm bones. "Kill the strongest first," Cornelisz had said. His burial confirmed that his had been among the early murders. Later victims were thrown to the sharks. Perhaps they lured him from his tent, or ambushed him as he went to relieve himself in the night, and in the morning all that remained were a few scuffed footmarks on the beach and a patch of new-turned coral soil. Did he cry out while they were murdering him, friendless in the dark? Did the others hear him in their tents and were they too afraid to help, telling themselves it was a seabird cry? How many more were in this pit of death? We asked Dave Johnson.

"I don't know," Dave said. "Quite a few, I expect. I found bits of them when I was putting the concrete down. They used to upset me a

* Ron Taylor recently won the World's Spearfishing Championship in Tahiti.

bit, but it was a question of getting used to them or moving the whole shack . . . I got used to them in time. Had to. They're all under concrete now." He grinned.

Our answering smiles were watery—we never got used to the corpses and slept restlessly above them, separated from the bones by the thin concrete floor and six inches of soil. Nightmares were frequent and divers often talked loudly and incoherently in their sleep, or woke up to find themselves sitting bolt upright and sweating in their sleeping bags while the wind keened and moaned outside the hut.

Ghosts? No one believed in them, they said. But there had been too much death on this island—murder, revenge, execution; it was a blood-soaked archipelago . . . islands of angry ghosts.

George and I had made jokes worthy of the grave-diggers scene in *Hamlet* when we began excavating, looking for the *Batavia* campsite. But we had hardly bargained for the macabre corpse we uncovered within a few minutes of turning the first shovelful of earth. The moment of truth when we uncovered the skull flung our irreverence back in our teeth. Death had the last laugh. He was lying right alongside the hut, and his head was only six inches under the sandy surface of Beacon Island. The bones were in a remarkable state of preservation, and the skeleton was complete except for the small bones of fingers and toes, which had been scattered by the burrowing birds which roosted on the island.

"I think he may be Andries de Vries," said Henrietta, who had hurried up with her notes, a scarf around her head, to see what was happening when we uncovered the skull. She peered and grimaced and flipped through the pages. "He was killed in just that way . . . July 14, 1629 . . . Look, here it is in the journal, in the confession of Lenert Michielsz" Paper fluttered in the wind as she read aloud. " 'Confesses that one day about noon (being 14 July last) has been called by Jan van Bemel into the tent of Jeronimus together with Jan Hendrixcsz and Rutger Fredricxsz and that he has ordered them to kill Andries de Vries, assistant. And that he has given them each a sword and a beaker of wine. Therefore they went to him, whereupon de Vries because he knew his life was in danger started to run—but Lenert Michielsz following him the quickest chiefly hacked him to death . . .' "

Poor, weak, Andries de Vries. He saved his life at the torment of his conscience after Jeronimus had sentenced him to be drowned by cutting the throats of the sick people in the infirmary tents at night. But he prolonged his own life for only a few wretched days.

"Of course he could be Bessel Jansz or Pauwels Barentsz or Claas Harmansz, who were hacked down the same way," Henrietta was muttering, leafing through her pages.

Naoom reported that our corpse had been a young man, tall and thin, probably under twenty years of age. This fitted de Vries' description, but so many men had died on this blood-stained island . . . (Twelve months after the expedition we were still finding human remains.)

"You can tell where the skeletons are," said Dave Johnson. "I find them when I'm burying rubbish. The soil has a characteristic dark greasiness."

There was a lot of that greasy soil on Beacon Island. We let the other corpses lie peacefully—with the exception of the now skull-less body Max had found on his famous reconnaissance expedition. This cadaver had a purse with two copper coins lying with it, and a flattened pistol bullet in its ribs. Its bones, too, were dusted and parceled up in a cardboard box. These bones were the grim evidence of murder done here, the irrefutable proof that this was the Batavia's Graveyard of Pelsaert's journal.

Digging strata-trenches across the island and shoveling the sand through sieves produced less gruesome relics of the old Hollanders. There were fire-blackened bird, seal and wallaby bones by the barrow load. The bird bones were mostly those of sooty-black mutton birds and fairy terns, delicate as a Japanese print, little strawlike leg bones browned and blackened on old coals, pathetic in their fragility. There would have been no more than a stringy fish-flavored mouthful of flesh on each bird, but the Dutchmen, hungry for meat, ate them ravenously after burning off the feathers in their fires. They were an excuse for murder more than once. The boy Andries de Bruyn had his throat cut on the moonlit beach by Allert Jansz, after he had been sent out into the night to catch birds for Cornelisz.

The islands are still a vast seabird rookery with terns, gannets, petrels, mutton birds, cormorants, pelicans and silver gulls by the hundred thousand. On West Wallabi Island the flocks wheeling and circling sometimes darken the sun. They float like great rafts on the sea by day. We would see them out on the ocean, hovering, fluttering, diving, following the schools of predatory fish, screeching and plunging to pick up the scraps from the slaughter as the sharks and mackerel and bonito chopped through the schools of small fish. They would come fluttering in, exhausted, long after nightfall, to their burrow-roosts in the soft soil of the islands, making soft pipings and twitterings as they landed on delicate wings. When we went out with a torch at night they would sometimes fly into us, blinded by the light, and lie trembling at our feet or in the crooks of our arms. We would put them gently on a bush, feeling the hearts panic, pulsing in the tiny bodies, and they would recover soon enough and flit to their burrows, squarking reproachfully . . . Eeeeh! . . . Eeeeh!

Old sleepy hair seals, with tawny coats, gray whiskers and enormous canine teeth—actually a breed of sea lion—still frequented the beaches of isolated islands, dozing in the sunshine. There were not nearly as many as when the Dutch came. The fishermen seldom molested them, but the seals preferred their own company, and when civilization came, they moved elsewhere. They were shy and suspicious of us on the beaches, but as soon as we were in the water swimming they became filled with lively curiosity and came and sniffed our flippers and rolled and frolicked, perhaps believing us to be a new species of seal. They were as friendly as huge spaniels, and had the same soft brown eyes. The Dutch saw them only as food; but who could blame shipwrecked men? They must have killed many of the poor beasts with pike and club. The thick bones of the seals, some still carrying old knife nicks, are legion in their fireplaces. We emptied dozens of haunch and chop bones out of the sieves.

Everyone on the island caught the digging bug. The Bevilaquas turned out with shovels and old Pop Marten, who found the first skeleton in 1960, though he was now in his 80's, was swinging a pick and turning over coral slabs with the rest of them. The Army men, bored with inactivity on the boat, came ashore and tried their hand. And between the multitudinous fragments of shell, coral and natural bird and animal bones, relics of the *Batavia* people mounted. There were fragments of glass and lead and brass, a piece of a pistol mechanism, a brass chain and a seal-stamp with what may have been a family crest.

"A seal . . . could that have belonged to van Huyssen, or those terrible boys, the van Welderens, whom the rest called the *jonkers,* the young noblemen?" Henrietta wondered aloud.

Death, death everywhere in this island, and over on Seal's Island, death too. There the gallows had been mounted. There Cornelisz and the others had died as they richly deserved, seeing for the last time over the water the island where they had perpetrated their horrible crimes, and, beyond it the reef with sections of the wreck still breaking through the surge . . . before the ladders and life were jerked away from under their feet. We had some arguments initially about which was "Execution Island," named Seal's Island by the Dutch. But reading through Henrietta's notes it became obvious that only the present-day Long Island across the channel from Beacon Island fitted the description.

Seal's must have been a big island (as distinct from some of the single-acre cays), because when the mutineers went "hunting" and killed forty folk on "Seal's Island" in successive beats, three boys hid under the bushes and saved themselves to the very last. The island today still has leafy bushes where a desperate fugitive might crouch. It straggles three quarters of a mile in length, though it is not more than 100 yards wide at the widest point, a high, spinelike ridge of shell, sand and bushes. Four men actually saved themselves from the Seal's Island massacre by throwing themselves into the water with pieces of wood and swimming—one of them wounded by a pike—across the shark channels to Weibbe Hayes', or West Wallabi, Island. They could only have done this from Long Island, where the length of the island and its outlying reefs would have prevented the mutineers from getting around in their boats to pursue and stop the refugees warning Hayes.

When the *Sardam* arrived, Seal's Island was used as a jail.

"They kept all the worst mutineers there except Cornelisz," said Henrietta. "It must have been a good, safe place because they were very afraid of them . . . fearing another mutiny. It stands to reason that they wouldn't have put the mutineers on any of the islets around the reef near Beacon because if they over-powered their guards and escaped from one of these at night, they could wade through the shallows and surprise Beacon Island. But they couldn't cross the twenty-three-fathom channel. They'd be safe over there and that's why I'm sure that Long Island is the Seal's Island of history." She tapped the pages of *Voyage to Disaster.* "And if you're still not convinced, here's the final proof—I quote you Pelsaert's journal, October 27, 1629: 'Therefore I ordered the smallest yawl to go to Seal's Island because they could see them [the *Sardam* at anchor under the High Island] better from there and give better signals from there. At last towards evening the yawl came, half an hour before sunset, and found that it was the fault of the Quartermaster who had been lying by the High Island so long beyond his orders and now it was too late' [to go to the wreck that day]."

There was no doubt about it, we agreed. The north end of Long Island *was* the closest point to the *Sardam* anchorage. This clearly established present-day Long Island as the Seal's Island or "Execution Island" of old.

"What about making a trip to Seal's Island and Weibbe Hayes' Island tomorrow?" suggested Merv Brown.

"A good idea," Max said. "The weather won't be much good for diving, I'm afraid—there was a big sea beating on the reef when I looked with the field glasses just before dinner tonight. Tomorrow would be as good a day as any to reconnoiter the other islands."

"I don't think there's much point in digging up any more dead men on Beacon Island," Graham Cramer agreed.

We had our proof and, though we knew there was a good deal more buried material, it was inconveniently located.

"I know what you're thinking," said Dave Johnson crossly. "But if you dig up those big bushes behind the shack you'll destroy my windbreak and there'll be more sand in here than the Sahara. And you're certainly not grubbing under my concrete floor. It took me a fortnight to put that down . . ."

"Now darling . . ." said Petra anxiously.

We soothed him. There was no need for the moment to dig him out of house and home. We knew where the bones and material were. Perhaps one day in the future the museum or a national historical trust might buy him out and we would excavate it. It was certain that there would be nothing more than cadavers, broken domestic ware, and a few worthless trinkets in the sandy soil. Pelsaert had been so desperate to salvage everything of value to placate those grim-jawed Councillors in Batavia, he had even had his men scour the island to pick up barrel hoops and woodwork. They went over Batavia's Graveyard with a fine-tooth comb. The frenzy for collecting next-to-worthless items had cost the lives of *Sardam* skipper Jacob Jacobsz and four men, lost with a yawl in a squall when sent to look for a barrel of vinegar.

"What about that little shelter place out on the sand spit?" asked Max, over the empty plates, coffee mugs, and sauce bottles of the dinner table, renewing an old controversy. He and his brother Graham had found buried stonework, like a giant fireplace, and skinning their hands on the coral and gnarled bushes—had excavated it to a depth of four feet. It had four eight-foot walls and a door in one corner. We couldn't imagine what its purpose was.

"A Chinaman's hut or built by a fisherman for smoking fish. Probably all of sixty years old," said Maurie Hammond, impishly baiting us, a beer glass in his hand and a cigarette dangling from his lips.

"There weren't any Chinamen on Beacon Island, because there was never any guano here," said Max rising to the lure. "Anyway no one would ever build a hut to live in down there. It's too close to the water, with crabs scuttling about and seabirds screeching. The obvious campsite is back here on the high ground where the old Dutch fire ashes are, and all the modern huts. And speaking from experience, you don't build a smokehouse *that* way."

Hammond winked.

"A lookout post for the survivors to watch the wreck and see if any barrels drifted in," suggested Merv Brown.

"That's more like it," said Max. "From the amount of earth and old timber we shifted out of there, it could easily be as old as the Dutchmen."

We argued about it half the night.

Next day we took stout boots against the razor shells (well-named) and wadcutters * of the shallows and the coral spikes of West Wallabi, and hats against the sun, and made our pilgrimage to Weibbe Hayes' Island, following the route the mutineers must have taken in their attacks. On the way we passed the modern crayfishing center of the Pigeon Islands (named by Wickham and Stokes because of the bronze-wing pigeons nesting there). They differ geologically from Beacon and the outlying cays; these islands are pure limestone, ringed by eight-foot undercut cliffs. They look like flat-topped mushrooms. The Pigeons were well-worked by the Chinese guano diggers. Today they are a crayfishing center and maritime slum, dotted with corrugated iron and

* Colloquial term for a marine worm which lives in mud in a hard lime tube with a sharp open end ¼ to ½ inch in diameter. Treading on it in squelching mud is like stepping on the sharpened end of a metal tube; it can remove neat circular hunks of flesh up to ½ inch into the foot, or simply break off and cause acute blood poisoning at a later stage. No one who has stepped on a wadcutter ever forgets it.

asbestos shanties, cliffs and foreshores piled high with old broken crayfish pots, rotting ropes, floats, flags and rusting iron ballast. Rickety jetties and landings extend out into the water. Corrugated iron lavatories balance above the sea on the edges of the low cliffs—perilous perches—and refuse and kitchen slops are thrown carelessly into the oil-slicked shallows. Rotting sheep heads, bullock hocks and fish, drying in the bait racks, waft putridly in the breeze. We wrinkled our noses as we passed.

The fishermen live on the islands for only part of the year, while the crayfish season is on. Most of them have pleasant homes in Geraldton on the mainland. The island huts were purely functional—somewhere to sleep at night—and the smell was part of any fishing industry. The fishing itself is hard, salt-weary work from dawn till dusk, and the fishermen grow sun-bleached beards and allow themselves and their huts to become unkempt. "We're out here to catch crayfish, not win house-and-garden competitions," they growl when reproached about the shaggy nature of the island. Some of the huts are lined, painted, and presentable inside, with gas stoves and kerosene refrigerators. Others are lined with sacking and have only the most primitive necessities for living. The fishermen flop down exhausted at night, and rise at dawn. Their waking world is tossing waves, the harsh glare of the sun, groaning winches, white floats and wicker crayfish pots. The crayfish they catch are frozen and sent to the United States, where they command a lucrative market among the night clubs and exclusive gourmet restaurants where the pale dinner-jacketed patrons and their minked ladies pay distorted prices for the tasty red crustacea they know as rock lobster. The hairy fishermen themselves rarely eat them. "We get sick o' the sight of the beggars," they say. Not that the fishermen don't dress in dinner jackets themselves at times. Some of them are rich men after years of successful fishing, and have expensive, modern homes and long American cars on the mainland. Most of them have an earthy wit, and the strong sense of independence typical of men who make their living from the sea the world over. It goes without saying that they are superb small boat seamen—their lives depend on it, working among the reefs and breakers where the crays are thickest, the waves biggest and frothiest. It was now the end of the season and the few boats in the anchorage showed the effects of the hard work in rust streaks, sun-peeled paint and hasty, temporary repairs to rigging and sea-damaged wheelhouses. In a few weeks they would be pulled up for repainting, barnacle scraping and refitting before the next season opened and the work began all over again.

We passed the boats, our bow waves spreading in v's of ripples across the yard-deep green shallows toward the long silhouette of Weibbe Hayes' Island. The mutineers had come this way, and we encountered some of the same problems. There were miles of shallow mud flats, slippery and spiked with shell and coral. These flats had continually frustrated the mutineers in their attempts to surprise Hayes' men, because they had to cross them at high tide and in daylight to see their way, giving the defenders plenty of time to prepare to meet them. The shallows were the reason the defenders were able to hold out against them—aided, too, by the low six-foot cliffs which formed a natural battlement from which to fight. We cursed our own way through the shallows, running aground with the engines roaring uselessly in coffee-colored swirls of mud, jumping out to push, slipping, falling into potholes up to our armpits . . . Finally we poled our way through the shallow strait between the two High Islands, East and West Wallabi, and approached through the deep-water anchorage on the north side, where there were more scattered crayfishermen's huts and a few boats at anchor.

The fishermen received us hospitably, made a cup of tea for Henrietta and Petra, and told us that they knew of wells on the other side of the island. "It's a long walk and tough going," they warned us.

They were right. The map shows East and West Wallabi as two large land masses, each slightly longer than broad, West Wallabi three and a half miles long, East Wallabi a little less. Our walk to the wells took us over some two miles of country. We found the big island very different from the sandy outer cays. There were fifty-foot hills on the north, stunted trees and heavy scrub in sections, and in the middle a plain so riddled with mutton bird burrows and infested with stinging nettles that—stumbling, floundering, falling among the burrows—we almost gave up. The burrows tunneled under the soft sand so that when we trod on apparently firm ground, they would collapse and we would plunge in thigh-deep, frequently sprawled headlong in prostrate profanity among the nettles, which stung handsomely. Poor Petra in a skirt was especially vulnerable to the nettles, and turned back in tears. Henrietta, too, was discouraged.

We battled on until we reached the hard limestone ground and the wells, facing shallow bays on the other side of the island. They were natural cisterns, with narrow necks opening out into bell-shaped limestone caverns. There were several feet of water and a lot of dead wallaby and bird bones in the bottoms of them. The openings had been well battered around the edges by the hammers and crowbars of fishermen and mariners since the Dutchmen, and thus enlarged. But it puzzled us that it should have taken Weibbe Hayes' men nearly three weeks to find the water. Perhaps, accustomed to the green woods and dells of Europe they had been looking for cool running streams, while we, used to the harsh and barren Australian interior, knew that limestone sinkholes were among the few natural places where rainwater would collect, and would have smelled the sinkholes out in a short time. Even if the openings of the wells had been hidden, the flight of the birds at sunset—pigeons especially—should have been a telltale sign.

Weibbe Hayes' Island was jumping with wildlife. A dozen species of lizards scuttled over the stones, fat lazy carpet snakes—non-venomous junior pythons—basked in the sunshine, legions of seabirds circled, screeching indignation at our intrusion, quail shot from the grass at our feet with whirring wings, and wallabies hopped through the bushes ahead of us. Curious little creatures, these small kangeroos. Handsome and furry, they are properly known as tammars (*Thylogale eugenii*), carry their young in pouches like all marsupials, and stand about 2 ft. 6 in. high. The Dutch called them "cats" and clubbed dozens of them for food. "There were also some Beasts which they called cats with as nice a flavour as I have ever tasted," wrote the Predikant Bastiaensz in his letter after his rescue. Pelsaert himself described them in some detail from a natural history rather than a belly-appreciation point of view.

Moreover on these islands there are large numbers of Cats which are creatures of miraculous form, as big as a hare; the Head is similar to a Civet cat, the fore-paws are very short, about a finger long. They run on the flat of the joint of the hind leg, so that they are not quick in running. The tail is very long . . . if they are going to eat they sit on their hind legs and rake the food with the fore-paws and eat exactly the same as the Squirrels or apes do. Their manner of procreation in Very Miraculous. Yea, worthy to note; under the belly the females have a pouch into which one can put a hand, and in that she has nipples, where we have discovered that in there their Young Grow with the nipple in mouth, and have been found lying in the pouch some Which were only as large as a bean. But found the limbs of the small beast to be perfectly in proportion so that it is certain that they grow there at the nipple of the mammal and draw the food out of it until they are big enough and can run. Even when they are very big they still creep into the pouch when chased and the mother runs off with them.

He was wrong about the birth. The baby marsupials are born in the normal manner, not as a growth from the nipple. They arrive like a hairless, pink and minute mouse, and are at once transferred to the nipple inside the pouch. Pelsaert's mistake was understandable; Australian bushmen believed the same thing for more than 100 years, and you can still get an argument about it in some outback pubs today.

Other wildlife that interested our men included the fat oysters on the sea rocks.

"Crazy things, oysters," I said. "Nature's true hermaphrodites—they change their sex according to their mood or the season."

"Must be confusing for their friends," said George.

We arrived back at the boats in mid-afternoon, hot, leg-weary, nettle-stung, and with our enthusiasm for exploring the further reaches of the island considerably diminished. We agreed that it had all been very interesting, but that it was unlikely there would be any traces of Weibbe Hayes' occupation. Perhaps we were influenced by our aching calves—because we were wrong . . . It would be a year before we learned of our mistake.

We decided to head back toward Beacon Island to give skinny Seal's Island a thorough going-over. I went on ahead with Max and Henrietta in the fast aluminum dory, smacking over the wave tops in puffs of spray at twenty miles an hour with the blue Evinrude outboard singing happily on full throttle. We circumnavigated East Wallabi and ran down on Seal's Island with wind and sea behind from the northeast, landing on a narrow strip of beach and scrunching ashore over the corals.

We found the shelter almost immediately as we topped the first rise.

"Look at this!" I shouted to Max.

"Just like the one on Beacon but bigger," he said, puffing over the hill.

Henrietta hurried up, notebook in hand. "What do you think it is?" she asked.

Max shook his head.

Inspiration struck me. "Of course, of course!" I cried, running down the slope into the hollow where the curious construction of coral slabs lay half buried. Like a sheepfold, or a pen—a pen. That was the clue.

"What the blazes is biting you?" Max asked, exasperated and curious, following me down the slope.

"Can't you *see*?" I said. "A jail! The little one on Beacon Island was for Cornelisz, the arch-villain. That's why it's out on the end of the sandspit where no one in their right senses would normally want to be . . . out of earshot of the camp. Easy to guard. *This* is where they kept the rest of 'em, leg-ironed and chained in between trials." I waved an arm at it.

Max looked doubtful. "Romantic, exciting. But convince me more."

Henrietta was flipping through the pages of her *Voyage to Disaster* manuscript, looking for some passage or other, like a bird pecking at seed.

"Well, this is exactly opposite Beacon Island," I said. "The shortest distance to row and the only really suitable landing spot. And if you wanted to stick up a gallows, the only soft ground for sinking posts is over there on the ridge." I indicated a spot about seventy-five yards away. "What more reasonable place than this for a jail? Handy for everything. They may have thrown canvas over the top and had these walls to stop the mutineers breaking out under the bottom, or it may simply have had a roof of planks with more coral thrown on top."

"You're right about the gallows," Max conceded. "As a builder I was thinking the same thing myself. On ninety-nine per cent of the island you couldn't sink a decent hole in the coral slabs. But there's guano earth and soft sand on the ridge."

We looked up at it, eyes narrowed against the late afternoon sun. A weather-whitened and ancient fisherman's marker post leaned drunkenly on top of the ridge. It wasn't difficult to imagine the gallows trees there, stark against the sky.

"There are probably a few unpleasant ghosts here on moonlit nights," said Henrietta shivering. "It was the custom to leave them hanging in those days. They could probably see the corpses swinging in the wind from over on Batavia's Graveyard."

> Dry corpses rattling in the wind . . .
> The gulls would pick their bones-o, bones-o . . .

We left the island to the sunset and its ghosts and, arriving back on Beacon shore, tied up the boat and hurried straight down to the stonework at the end of the sandpit. It was a smaller twin of the one on

Seal's Island, identical in design and construction. The coral slabs were laid layer on layer, flat on top of each other, the way I had seen them in European sheepfolds. It was altogether different from the construction of some of the old stone fishermen's huts and guano ruins, built with round, heavy stones.

"Here's the passage I was looking for," said Henrietta at last, sitting on one of the walls to read.

"Cornelisz *was* kept in a prison . . . listen . . . Three nights before he was hanged he raged that 'God will not suffer that I shall die a shameful death' . . . so Pelsaert rightly feared an attempt at suicide; 'Therefore I ordered the Guard that no-one should hand him a knife or anything with which he could damage himself. But at night he secretly ate something with which he thought to poison himself for it started to work about one o'clock in the morning, so that he was full of pain and seemed like to die. In great anxiety he asked for some Venetian theriac [antidote]. At last he began to get some relief because apparently the poison had not been strong enough. But he had to be got out of his PRISON [Henrietta emphasized] certainly 20 times during the night because his so-called miracle was working from below as well as from above. . . .' There you are." Henrietta snapped the pages shut triumphantly.

We looked down on the old gray walls, the prison where malevolent, scheming Jeronimus Cornelisz spent the last wretched and manacled days of his life in an agony of counter-accusation of his fellow plotters and fear of the fate which waited inexorably for him on the island over the water . . .

22 GREAT FINDS AND GREAT DANGER

The waves sighed over the reef. The crabs scuttled, the anemones waved their poison tendrils in the current, the corals glowed softly; fish flickered, sharks and bonito patrolled the no man's land on the edge of the purple deeps . . . overhead the gulls hovered, sharp-beaked, sharp-eyed . . . watching . . . The day-to-day cycle of life went on as it had every day for a thousand, a million years, storm following calm and calm following storm, the south wind moving to the east, then the north, then around by the west back to the south . . . But to us it was now a matter of less than a week. Every day was important, and we were running out of time.

The wise old sea eagles which watched the sea daily, resting on their wings on the thermals 1000 feet up, could have told us: "If it is not calm tomorrow, it will be calm the day after or the week after or the month after. That is the Law of Things. Be patient." But we could not be patient, and we were worried because the Navy was delayed.

In our crazy man-made world where every minute is scheduled, organized down to the last acid bite of the ulcer, we had until the end of the week and no more than that. So we worried. George Brenzi had to get back to his trucks. Max had a contract to build a house. Merv Brown had to report at 8:30 on a certain morning to the printing office. Maurie Hammond had to return to taking routine newspaper photographs of motor smashes, brides, footballers, and baby-kissing politicians. I had a vacant desk and typewriter. Naoom had patients already rehearsing the opening lines of their symptoms. A dozen jobs waited in Jack Sue's engineering shop for his decision. The Army and Navy had their orders. And there were wives and children . . . and gardens untended, letters unanswered, bills unpaid . . . So that instead of sitting cross-legged on our island in Confucian calm waiting sensibly and unworried for the cloudless blue day suitable for final cannon lifting, we knotted our stomachs in impotent anxiety, and grew testy.

A new mast was the Navy's trouble. The mast cracked and bent by our cannon was a wooden one. It would cost much to repair, and having been badly strained once might never be reliable again. For very little extra cost they could have a steel mast, brand-spanking-new and able to lift any cannon with ease. The decision was obvious, but before the new mast could be installed it had to be approved at Navy HQ. Signals had to be sent to important men in gold-trimmed hats, forms had to be filled in, requisition orders made out—while Hec and his crew had to wait chafing at the wharf in Geraldton. Then, when they got permission, the installation and testing of the new mast took longer than expected. It was not the fault of Hec Donohue or the Navy, but time and tide, which wait for no mast, rolled merrily along and the fact that the sea weather remained fine at the wreck did nothing to relieve our anxiety. Though we had cleared four bronze guns to a safe spot away from the breaking surf of the reef, the new-masted GPV would still need a flat sea to load them.

"It just can't stay calm at this time of the year for so long—it's unnatural. We must be building up for a blow," groaned Max.

Cal Hoven, a genial ex-American Air Force technician who had arrived after the Navy's departure said, "I guess you're right. We'd better dive while we can."

So we went diving. And the most significant find of the expedition for the moment eclipsed the worry over whether we'd be able to get the guns out of the ocean. Ironically it was an object I almost discarded as being unworthy of salvaging.

We were working along the keel of the wreck again, burrowing into the soft coral, freeing a few more sea-eaten powder canisters and pieces of pottery. George had sifted out some coins, and generally speaking we had a reasonable haul, without finding anything spectacular. Maurie Hammond was hard at work photographing us among some picturesque corals a little distance from the wreck. After the picture-taking was over I picked up some of the things we had freed from the reef and was swimming back with them towards the keel of the aluminum boat below the surface, when my eye was caught by a piece of bright green on the bottom. A coin? I dived to investigate. It wasn't a coin but a corner of unidentifiable brass—A head-sized lump, corroded and swollen. Jolly heavy and hardly important, I thought. I let it fall back to the bottom, stirring up a little cloud of sand as it bumped and rolled down the coral slope. But when I had delivered the other pieces to the boat, conscience pricked. It might be something after all. Better make sure . . . So I flippered back again and picked it up.

When we got it ashore, Chris Halls, bushy eyebrows bunched so that I thought they'd remain permanently fused together, said, "Good Heavens! This may be the most important find of the whole expedition!"

"What is it?" asked Merv.

"An astrolabe."

"A what. . . ?" asked Maurie, screwing up his face.

"An astrolabe, man. A navigation instrument . . . for determining the angle of the sun or a star to get latitude." Chris explained so rapidly that his words fell over each other, as he caressed the green thing with his hands. "It was a forerunner of the sextant. They're very rare, and there are only a few surviving specimens scattered among museums around the world. This is a very important discovery!"

We had never seen him so excited.

With the encrustation chipped away, it was a piece of brass shaped like a wheel, with four spokes. And it was heavy, weighing about eight pounds.

"How did it work?" asked Max, ever practical.

"The skipper would hold it dangling from his thumb by a ring, with the sun coming over his left shoulder," Chris explained. "The edge of the circle faced the sun, and he would shift the moving alidade arm—most of this one has crumbled away—until the sun shone through both the peepholes on it at noon. The angle that the arm indicated on the marked gradations around the wheel rim then showed the highest point of the sun and from this it was possible to work out its angle and from this the distance north or south of the equator."

We handled it in turn. It was green with corrosion, warted with sea growth, but suddenly beautiful in our eyes. (Months later, Lieutenant Commander D.W. Waters RN, Curator of Navigation at Britain's

Greenwich National Maritime Museum, and Professor D.J. Price, History of Science chairman at Yale University, confirmed Chris's opinion about the astrolabe's rarity and historical value.)

The discovery restored our good cheer, and after lunch our spirits were further revived by a TOOT! TOOT! TOOT! as the fat, gray old Navy GPV wallowed sedately down the channel. It was six days since we had seen her.

Hec apologized for the delay over a mug of coffee. "Anyway," he said brightly, "it's a beautiful day. We'll jerk those cannon out this afternoon."

But our good luck of the first week had deserted us. We found the raft half-sunk; some of the bungs had been alloy instead of the cast-iron we had specified, and in sea water electrolysis between them and the steel had eaten them away. We had to bring the raft in and work until midnight on it, emptying out drums and fitting steel bungs borrowed from crayfishermen's empty fuel drums.

"The barometer's falling like a stone," said Dave Johnson uneasily.

At dawn we heard the surf on the reef, booming like the cannon of a ship in distress. The wind whistled shrilly, angrily, and in the increasing light of dawn we could see whitecaps whipped off the waves in the lagoon. Over on Noon Reef the spray was spouting forty feet in the air. Binoculars showed a maelstrom of foam with three lines of breakers over the *Batavia.*

"What rotten luck!" said Hec bitterly, coming ashore after breakfast.

We nodded glumly and prepared for a day shore-bound; yet by lunchtime the eye-stinging sou'easter had dropped, in one of those sudden, surprising weather changes that can come in the islands. The sun was out and the lagoon calm and peaceful.

"It looks beautiful," said Naoom in amazement. "Incredible; I couldn't believe weather would change so quickly."

Maurie Hammond squinted out like a wise old owl at the swells still lumping the horizon and shook his head. "A waste of time going out," he said. "You might even get drowned. It's just that sort of day."

They looked at him, and then back at the water sparkling in the warm sunshine. Arguments with Hammond tended to be prolonged affairs, so they said nothing; but obviously they didn't believe him.

"It will be rougher than you think," warned Dave Johnson, "but we'll give it a try."

"Well, we can always come back in if it's too rough," said Merv, rubbing his moustache.

"Nothing ventured, nothing gained," said Hec. "Come on."

So out we went, Dave's boat loaded with the Navy men, the Army SAS chaps Dugdale, Aitken and Urquhart in their outboard-powered rubber assault craft, and myself, Jack Sue and Merv Brown in the de Havilland aluminum boat. Dave was towing the repaired raft with Pappy Gault and Maurie Giles sitting aboard.

Personally, I had a few misgivings, an instinct that things were not altogether right. I had had enough experience with Abrolhos reefs to know that there was a very much bigger sea still running out there than most of the men realized. The wind had dropped as quickly as it had come, but it took time for the angry swells to subside, and the first blow may have been merely a breath of a bigger storm to come. It happened that way sometimes in the islands. That was how Jacob Jacobsz drowned in 1629. But as they had said, if it was rough we could always turn back. We would reproach ourselves later if we missed a chance on the guns.

As soon as we rounded the corner reefs out of Goss Passage, I knew that there would be trouble if we persisted. An ugly, glassy swell was rolling, and I had to go a quarter of a mile farther out to sea than usual before I turned to run with the breakers. Looking back I saw that Dave, slowed by towing the pontoon raft, was disappearing from our sight below successive wave crests.

At the wreck there was a twenty-foot rise and fall in swell. I had only a forty-foot anchor rope and a light anchor. "I can't possibly anchor this boat here," I said to Merv and Jack. "She'll either swamp or jerk the hook out of the bottom and go up on the reef. The only thing to do is to keep the motor running and circle . . ." My words were drowned out by a monster breaker that crashed in foam and spray, leaving a 300-yard-wide belt of eddying white water right across the wrecksite.

"My God! Look at that!" said Jack.

"That settles it for me," I said. "It's not worth the risk in there with a three-ton cannon frisking about the bottom. It'll kill someone."

But when the crayboat chugged up with her tow, the Navy boys made signs to indicate that they were going in. I drew alongside and shouted a warning. "There's a pretty big surf running!"

The words were no sooner out of my mouth than we were wallowing in the middle of one of the treacherously calm spells that can come on windless days with big breakers. There was no sign of the viciousness of a few minutes before. It was as though the ocean was trying to lure us into the trap.

"Looks all right to me," said Hec.

I should have told them it was too damn dangerous, but instead I shrugged.

"Well, I suppose I'd better go in and show the flag," said Merv without enthusiasm.

"I'll keep circling, and rescue you when the time comes—if I can," I said grimly.

The divers rolled over the side, disappearing with splashes. Only bubbles were visible, but Jack and I knew what they would be doing down there. They would have swum over to the big bronze cannon lying in its coral bed, would be looping around it the thick wire slings, looking around for the hook of the cannon-raising raft, dangling and bobbing from the opaque ceiling of the surface, in order to link the two.

"If the waves only hold off for another five minutes, they might just fluke it," said Jack. We began to feel guilty about not being in with them. We were going to look pretty silly with our talk of rescue roles.

Then a sixth sense began to prickle. "It's been calm too long," I said uneasily. "I don't like it."

Now we could see that the cannon had been hooked on. Maurie Giles was winding on the winch. In a minute the cannon would jerk and grind off the bottom in a cloud of debris and coral dust, swinging angrily.

"LOOK OUT!" shouted Jack in alarm. Instinctively I gave the motor full throttle and spun the boat in her own length.

Out at sea was a towering wave, the top beginning to run white already as it curved to break. It looked about twenty feet high and I knew that unless we reached it before it attained its critical angle, we would be flung backward before it in our light craft and smashed on the reef in a boil of foam. We made it—just—taking water over the bow and stern, and with the de Havilland rearing to such an alarming angle that Jack in the bow nearly fell on top of me in the stern. We came close to flipping over backward.

"God Almighty!"

We were both shaken as we tumbled down the steep back slope of the wave. Then we saw another wave, even bigger, just behind it.

How we weathered that second one I'll never know. Looking back I saw Dave's crew desperately trying to cast off the raft tow rope and race for it as we had. The wave curled and crashed with a tremendous roar. "They're gone!" Jack exclaimed, then—welcome sight—the bluff bow of Dave's sturdy little boat broke through the foam. She had been buried by the wave but her weight had carried her through where our light fourteen-footer would have been swept before it and smashed like tinsel. But even as Dave's boat and its ashen occupants rode through the foam, I saw the wave pick up the raft like a toy, drag it, throw it high in the air, and then tumble it over and over toward the maelstrom of the reef.

"Maurie and Pappy!" I said, feeling sick.

Neither of them had flippers on. If they had been under the raft when it overturned, they must surely have been crushed. . . .

There was a moment's awful nothingness; then the black heads of divers began to bob up in the foam like footballs in a snowfield. Immediately arms waved distress signals. I was sure someone had been killed or drowned. Racing in, we grabbed two men at a time on the metal rails attached to the gunwhales, and without taking them aboard dragged them out to the deeper, safer region seaward. Twice we had to get them to let go and run for it again, as other breakers threatened. The rubber boat was doing the same thing; on the third run I saw the welcome sight of one of the Army men dragging Maurie Giles into it by the seat of his overalls, and Pappy swimming strongly nearby. ("Out of the water to the third button of his overalls, by God, and passing all of us even without flippers," Hec said later when we could joke about it.) Maurie looked shaken but unharmed. Later we learned that both of them had been completely upside-down under the raft when it took off with the cannon like a crazy thing. It jerked the cannon seventy-five yards across the reef before the slings parted and the raft flew up in the air. Somewhere along the way, as Pappy and Maurie bailed out, the 250-pound winch brushed the back of Maurie's head as it fell . . . a very narrow escape!

The divers had an equally close shave. "The cannon went wild. We couldn't see it because the water was just like the inside of a cream meringue with froth . . . impossible to tell which was up or down or which way to swim," Merv gasped when we got him aboard. Merv, unlike most Australian divers, can only swim a few yards without his flippers! If he'd lost them in that mess. . . .

One by one we picked up all the divers; amazingly everyone was present and undamaged. We cracked a few shaky jokes, laughed unconvincingly, looked disconsolately at the spot where our raft had disappeared, and turned for home. On our way in we saw the two-ton raft, thrown on its back like a discarded toy or an unpended turtle on the wrong side of the reef.

Maurie Hammond was waiting with his hands on his hips at the jetty. "You silly bastards," he said, shaking his head.

That night the wind blew shrieking across the island.

"Someone will get killed on that wreck," Jack said somberly in the lamplight. I noticed the others touching the wooden table. A bad sign.

"That's right, you know," said Chris Halls. "You've got the finest collection of relics ever taken from an Australian shipwreck. Why don't you call it quits, before someone gets hurt? Maybe come back some other day?"

"Time, the old enemy," I said wryly.

Our days were up, and I knew it was time to go home. But the wreck still tempted . . . Just one more day, and who could tell what we might find.

There is a time to stop with everything; the thing is to be able to recognize it. It was time to wind up the *Batavia* expedition. We had accomplished a great deal—far more than we or anyone else had expected. The only thing that could mar our triumph now was an accident. The men were at the stage where they were likely to have an accident. Hard diving and the constant excitement and tension had done it. Their hair was stiff and dry as straw from long hours in the water, and they were tired, much more tired than they would admit, from the nervous and physical strain. They were beginning to take risks, to lose the edge of their cool precision. So far it had only been noticeable in little things; but next time it might be a big thing and someone might come back in one of the boats the pathetic, floppy object in a rubber suit that is a dead diver. I had seen it before and the memory was burned into my brain. "Wait for the calm day," the sea eagles would have said. And if it didn't come, there would always be another day and another time. The sea does things in its own way, and man cannot bend it to his will.

"Perhaps we can get a last dive in tomorrow," said Max as we cleaned our teeth outside the hut before going to bed.

I doubted it, and he did not really believe it. The wind flapped our towels around our shoulders and moaned in the bushes.

When we woke in the morning—our last full day, since the others would have to go aboard the Army boat at noon the next day—the wind shrilled derisively at us. It came from the southeast, the worst direction for the wreck, and so no one dived. We wandered about packing gear, filling chests of sawdust with relics and hating the weather. Later we managed to salvage the raft from its position of upside-down indignity on the reef and tow it back through the shallows.

"Maybe we'll dive tomorrow in the morning, before we leave," said Max.

But in the morning a full storm was raging. We had agreed that Maurie and I would stay behind with the Navy to load the four cannon dumped away from the reef, and pack up the gear—the ceremonial finalities to an expedition already finished. The others who had more urgent commitments would leave on the Army boat. None of them wanted to go, but that was the way it was and they had to.

Now frightening seas from the north were surging down through the passage. Dave Johnson and another fisherman, Alan Martin, used their crayboats as taxis and ran the fellows across the 23-fathom channel through the spray and spume, taking a tremendous buffeting. We waved them off. "We hate to leave you," they said, and meant it.

"Cheerio, chaps, and thanks for everything," I replied. I had something of a lump in my throat. If we had been Frenchmen or Italians we would have embraced each other and wept at the parting as the end of something rather splendid and not to be recaptured. Being dour Anglo-Saxons we repressed our emotions and forced a casual and offhand manner we were far from feeling. It must have been like that at the end of the war, I thought, when the squadrons and good units broke up.

They sailed off into the storm.

By nightfall, and life's irony, the weather had broken and blue patches were appearing in the sky. The next day was serene and we loaded three of the cannon with minimum trouble in a beautiful sea.

Next morning we grappled the fourth aboard so easily and smoothly it was like a dream. I salvaged the fallen raft winch from the surf with the aid of a drum and a Honolulu surf ride on a big breaker, taking some risks to absurdly square with my conscience for not having been in on the day of the big waves. And suddenly it was time for us to go, too.

There was the last job of packing up our gear and loading it back on the GPV, tackled with far less enthusiasm than the unloading two weeks before. The aluminum surf tender that had served us so well was hoisted to lie turtle-fashion across the deck; Dave's boat was tethered behind like a fractious horse (he and Petra were coming back to Geraldton with us); and the grim old guns lay below in the bottom of the hold with their crests and scrolls and barnacles. We hoisted the anchor, spun the helm, saluted, and the diesel rose to a crescendo of departing power as the GPV gathered her skirts and picked up her seven knots of maximum speed.

I looked back as the low silhouette of Beacon Island dropped astern.

"It's all over," said Hec quietly.

"Yes," I said. "It's finished."

23 | A SHARK ATTEMPTS TO FINISH AN UNFINISHED STORY

There was an aftermath, of course.

We came home happy, but very tired after the concentrated diving, with sun-bleached hair, wrinkled, salt-damp clothes and a far-away look in our eyes. Our minds were still full of the things we had seen and done.

Our immediate ambition aimed no higher than a week of sleep and hot baths. But we suffered a period of brief fame. TV interviewers slung microphones around our unwilling necks and asked odd questions; some important people looked at our relics and posed for photographs with them; our skull grinned from news pages.

At first we found it extraordinarily difficult to talk about our experiences. We were still too close to them. For a few days we moved in a curious vacuum in which our minds were still oriented to the corals and breakers of the Abrolhos; our bodies moved like strangers among the tall buildings, the noisy traffic hell-bent between Stop-Go lights, and the rivers of anonymous faces along the city pavements.

All of us felt it in different ways. I came to dread the introductions: "Mr. Edwards is just back from discovering doubloons on the *Batavia* wreck. He'll tell you all about it."

The questions often made me feel claustrophobic in a way I never experienced underwater.

"Doesn't it terrify you down there—all those sharks and things?"

The denizens were less terrifying than a businessmen's luncheon or a roomful of strange, expectant people at a cocktail party.

"How much are you selling your coins for, buddy? The papers said you got sackfuls. Aw, come on . . . just one won't hurt."

"What's your angle in all this? What do you *get* out of it?"

Get out of it . . . ! That was the most frequent and the hardest question to answer. It is almost impossible to answer people who would ask such a question. The non-profit fascination of a wreck like the *Batavia,* the comradeship of the diving, the excitement of important discoveries—these were the things we had "got" out of it.

We kept two coins each as mementoes. The rest of the relics, some of which were extremely valuable, went to the West Australian Museum. The Geraldton Council mounted the finest of the bronze guns outside their civic center. The Navy kept another for their HMAS Leeuwin parade ground, to gleam with the spit and polish of future generations of naval cadets.

"You're crazy to hand the stuff over—it would be worth a fortune in antique shops," certain acquaintances accused me at the time.

Our minds resented the swiftness of the transition from wave-spiked horizons and wild island sunsets to the jackdaw meaningless chatter of sophisticated life in town. Even with people who really cared it was difficult at first. As Merv said sadly: "How do you explain to someone who's never been underwater what it was like with the staghorn coral and the silver bream wheeling about and the sunlight coming dappled through onto the bronze guns. Or describe a branch of staghorn like a reindeer's antler covered with little blue lights?"

We were oversensitive, like eyes suddenly exposed to a bright light. Perhaps we were also a little jealous of our wreck and not ready yet to share it with strangers. But, as eye pupils gradually accustom to the glare, so we adjusted. In a few days we had made the transition and the silly questions became a joke for which we evolved lighthearted answers of an acceptable kind. We found, with people who were seriously interested, that imagination is a boundless thing, and it didn't matter a scrap that they hadn't been underwater or on the wreck. We were able to talk intelligently and informatively with them. Merv became quite glib with his description of staghorn coral.

We were a seven-day wonder. Then the grasshopper of public interest skipped on. We were grateful for the return to normalcy.

"Thank heaven you'll be able to stay at home and do something in the garden," said my wife. "That side hedge. . . !"

"Yes, dear," I said absently, already thinking about the next trip to the wreck.

While summer southerlies shrouded the wreck reef in spray, we planned a new assault from far away, dreaming with hedge-clippers in our hands.

A year later, in August, 1964 (the time of the calm water), we were among the familiar island silhouettes of the Abrolhos again. Max and Graham Cramer, Merv Brown, Maurie Glazier and I went across aboard Frank Bombara's crayfish carrier boat *Emmalou* with our diving gear and aluminum boat, together with a cheerful bunch of Aquinas College kids going to do a nature survey of the islands for a school holiday project. My research over the summer in the State Archives had turned up the information that there were unidentified ruined walls on a section of West Wallabi Island where people seldom went. They were noted in 1879 and said to be ancient then. Could they be Weibbe Hayes' defenses? We had to find out.

Again our luck held. We found the walls and they were Dutch—the age-grayed stone forts on Weibbe Hayes' Island. They were identified as built by *Batavia* people by a broken Bellarmine jug buried in the sandy floor of one of them. The crest on the pottery fragment was identical to those we had found on the wreck. This fort or shelter overlooked a little sandy bay. It was of the same curious construction of flat flags of stone as the stonework on Beacon Island and Seal's Island and the pottery proved their Dutch origin as well. The fort identified the bay where Cornelisz had come ashore with his lieutenants to make a fake "peace" with the defenders, giving them cloth and wine and lying promises while Davidt Zeevanck and Coenraat van Huyssen tried to buy the French soldiers with 6000 guilders apiece in *Batavia* silver. The bones of Cornelisz' men were probably buried here where they were killed on this beach—now deserted except for crabs and seagulls and looking as though nothing more dramatic than the killing of little lizards by sea eagles had taken place over thousands of years. Terns nested in mangrove trees on the island where the mutineers had stood and watched.

Out on the wreck the seas dropped to a flat calm so that, as Pelsaert wrote in his journal on a similar day, "it was like a miracle." We anchored the faithful de Havilland surf boat over the wreck. Before Maurie Glazier and I had pulled on our flippers, Max and Graham Cramer, first into the water, had surfaced, grinning and dripping, and waving a green object. "Another astrolabe!" Max shouted.

Sand had washed away since the year before and exposed it.

This one was a new, half-moon-shaped variety previously uncatalogued which promised to cause a stir among the navigation experts on the other side of the world. We found a brass dish and more powder canisters as well as evidence of more brass and pottery buried under the reef, which we marked down for future excavation.

And there was the incident of the shark.

I am always reminded since of the limerick which runs . . .

> There was a young man of Bengal,
> Who went to a fancy dress ball;
> He thought he would risk it
> And go as a biscuit,
> But a dog ate him up in the hall.

The attack came after ten years of comparative immunity from man-eaters, a period in which I had encountered some hundreds and in fact had killed half a dozen big ones. It all seemed so absurdly unreal and nightmarish, like that last line of the limerick. But it was real enough and serious enough.

Max and I had gone to our jewfish hole at the end of Seal's Island with spearguns to catch our dinner. There the water sloped away over an underwater cliff from green shallows to seventy feet and a ledge and away from that again into who-knows-what-depth of murky black water. I had always thought of it as a sinister place, but there were good jewfish there the year before, and we were tired of tinned meat and tempted into indiscretion. This year the bottom was empty of jewfish. I made dives to sixty feet and, peering about in disturbingly dark water, saw no telltale silvery tails waving in the current. Max gave up in disgust and swam back to the boat. "Better pack it in—it's too late to be swimming in this kind of water," he warned on the surface. I dived again, was poised over a volcanolike knoll at the edge of the seventy-foot ledge—dark, evil water misty below me—and was considering following him when the shark appeared on the edge of my vision, coming up out of the deep and moving very fast. I swung to meet him, following the old routine which had proved itself dozens of times before: Stick your speargun out in front; make yourself look as big as possible; growl to convince yourself if you like; then swim right at your shark as though you mean to eat *him*. He will circle nervously and depart, convinced that you are a dangerous animal.

This shark was the exception.

He stood my bluff with watchful, yellow eyes, and as I closed, turned his pig head up toward me in a horrible, inquiring manner. He was about eight or nine feet long, thick as a barrel, with long gill slits—a whaler shark, genus *Carcharhinus,* with the words "Dangerous to Man" written against his name in the textbooks.

I ran out of breath—we don't use breathing apparatus when fishing—and ascended to the surface, watching him closely. Suddenly without warning and without any of the usual preliminary circling, he attacked. A tremendous lunge of his squab body had him inside my guard and smashing up under my flippers from behind before I could bring my speargun around to fire. I heaved and squirmed, trying to find room for my five-foot spear between me and him, and flailed my flippers in desperation, trying to prevent him from getting to my thigh and taking that fatal artery-slashing bite into the hamstring muscles at the back of the leg. Somehow I got the gun around and with a controlled effort sent the spear thudding into his side, through his left pectoral fin and out again. There was no chance to reload.

He swirled me aside in an explosion of muscled power and I tensed for the recoil attack. It didn't come. Instead he sounded down into the black water. I had hurt him more than I thought; he was shaking his ugly head like a groggy boxer trying to clear his eyes and trailing blood in his wake.

I retrieved my bent spear and gun and retreated to the boat.

"The cheeky bastard!" I said, sitting on the boat. But my hands were shaking when I took my mask and flippers off.

It was my own fault. Swimming alone in dark, deep water with the sun sinking below the horizon (I had told others dozens of times when giving advice), was just asking for trouble.

The sea had taught me a sharp lesson, given me a slap for my overconfidence—for divers owe more deaths to overfamiliarity than any other cause.

It is a savage, pristine world down in the sea with the corals. We leave our man-made rules behind when we venture into it.

Maybe one day the sea may take the lives of one of our divers. A risk we must accept, for in a way, we are part of the sea ourselves.

There are years of work on the wreck ahead: photographing, surveying, bringing up more relics from untouched sections of reef as the sea permits. And those 8000 rix dollars remain a challenge for someone.

Ashore there is the task of setting up a maritime museum worthy of the ship—for the coins, cannon, navigation instruments, the skulls, the photographs—to let other people share our adventure in diving on the wreck of the *Batavia* without getting their feet wet (or being eaten up by a shark in the hall).

For us, of course, there will always be a new wreck on a new reef. Somewhere.

BIBLIOGRAPHY

Historical References

Battye, J. S., *Western Australia,* Oxford, 1924.
Bligh, William, *The Mutiny On Board HMS Bounty,* New York, 1962.
Chester, Alan, *Brother Captain,* London, 1964.
Cohen, B. C., "The Discovery of Western Australia with Some Early Medical History," *Australian Medical Journal,* June, 1953.
de Heer, C. (translator), *The Zeewyk Log, Adriaen van der Graeff, 1727–28,* translated in 1963 by Mr. de Heer of W. A. University (Courtesy B. Goppel, Rotterdam).
Drake-Brockman, Henrietta, "The Reports of Francisco Pelsaert," *Early Days: Journal and Proceedings,* WA Historical Society, Perth, 1956.
———, *Voyage to Disaster,* Sydney, 1963.
———, *The Wicked and the Fair,* Sydney, 1957.
———, "The Wreck of the Batavia," *Walkabout Magazine,* Melbourne, 1955.
Edwards, Hugh, *Gods and Little Fishes,* London, 1962.
Forrest, John, "Report on a Visit to the Abrolhos Islands, 1879," Western Australian State Archives.
Grey, G., *Journals of Discovery,* London, 1941.
Goldsmith, F. H., *Treasure Lies Buried Here,* Perth, 1946.
Gordon, W. J., *The Captain General,* London, 1888.
Halls, C., articles in the *Countryman* (Western Australia) under the pen name Marcus Conrad.
Heeres, J. E., *The Part Borne by the Dutch in the Discovery of Australia, 1606–1765,* Leiden and London, 1899.
Jansz, Jan, *Ongeluckige Voyagie van't Schip Batavia,* Amsterdam, 1647.
MacLiesh, F. and Krieger, M., *Fabulous Voyage,* London, 1963.
Major, R. H., *Early Voyages to Terra Australia,* London, 1859.
Pascoe, Commander J. Crawford, R. N., *A Roving Commission,* Melbourne, 1897.
Playford, Dr. P. E., "The Wreck of the Zuytdorp on the Western Australian Coast in 1712," *Early Days,* WA Historical Society, 1959.
Siebenhaar, W., *The Abrolhos Tragedy* (his translation of Jansz, published in *Western Mail,* Perth, 1897).
Somerville, W., *Rottnest Island in History and Legend,* Perth, 1949.

Stokes, Lort J., *Discoveries In Australia*, London, 1837.
Taunton, H., *Australind*, London, 1903.
Uren, Malcolm, *Sailormen's Ghosts*, Melbourne, 1940.
Wilson, S. J., "The Significance of Coins in Identification of Old Dutch Wrecks on the Western Australian Coast," *Spinks Numismatic Circular*, September, 1964.

Diving or General Interest References

Carson, Rachel, *Under the Sea Wind*, London, 1952.
———, *The Edge of the Sea*, London, 1955.
Clarke, Arthur C., *The Treasure of the Great Reef*, London, 1964.
Coppelson, Dr. V. M., *Shark Attack*, Sydney, 1958.
Cousteau, Jacques-Yves, *The Living Sea*, London, 1963.
——— and Dumas, F., *The Silent World*, New York, 1963, and other works.
Cropp, Ben, *The Shark Hunters*, Adelaide, 1964.
Davis, Sir R. H., *Deep Diving and Submarine Operations*, London, 1956.
Dakin, W. J., *Australian Sea Shores*, Sydney, 1963.
Diolé, Philippe, *The Undersea Adventure*, London, 1953.
Douglas, John Scott, *The Story of the Oceans*, London, 1953.
Dugan, James, *Man Explores the Sea*, London, 1956.
Falcon-Barker, Captain E., *1600 Years Under the Sea*, London, 1960.
Goadby, Peter, *Sharks and Other Predatory Fish of Australia*, Brisbane, 1959.
Hass, Hans, *Expedition into the Unknown*, London, 1965, and other works.
Hill, Ralph Nading, *Window In the Sea*, London, 1956.
Life Nature Library, *The Sea*, Netherlands, 1963.
Lilly, Dr. John C., *Man and Dolphin*, New York, 1961.
Oceans, various contributors, London, 1962.
Phillips, Craig, *The Captive Sea*, London, 1965.
Roughley, T. C., *Fish and Fisheries of Australia*, Sydney, 1951.
Taylor, J. Du Plat, *Marine Archaeology*, London, 1965.
United States Navy, *Submarine Medicine Practice*, Washington, 1956.
Webster, David Kenyon, *Myth and Maneater*, London, 1962.

INDEX

A NOTE ABOUT THE AUTHOR

Hugh Edwards is an award-winning writer and marine photographer from Perth, Western Australia. His love of diving has involved him in many underwater ventures, ranging from marine archaeology in the Mediterranean to filming sharks in Australian coastal waters.

He played a major part in the discovery of the famous Silver Ships, the Dutch vessels that were shipwrecked off the Western Australian coast in the seventeenth and eighteenth centuries.

In *Islands of Angry Ghosts* he describes the most significant of these expeditions, the surveying of the *Batavia* (1629), which uncovered a grim tale of mutiny and massacre on lonely coral islands. This work won the Sir Thomas White Memorial Prize for the Best Book written by an Australian in 1966.

Hugh Edwards' twenty-one books cover a wide range of topics, including Aboriginal legends, historical subjects and children's fiction. He has also worked on many television productions.

In 1994 as a result of recommendations by a Western Australian Parliamentary Select Committee on Ancient Shipwrecks, Hugh Edwards was given an award of $25,000 for his role in the discovery of the *Batavia*. In 1996 he was presented with Certificates of Merit by the Western Australian Government, officially recognising him as a primary discoverer of the *Batavia* and the 1727 *Zeewyk* which was also wrecked in the Abrolhos Islands.

Hugh Edwards has also been awarded the Lovekin Prize for Journalism in 1964, the Western Australia Week Non-Fiction Award in 1984 (shared) for *Port of Pearls* and the Best Australian Television Documentary in 1980 for *Wreck at Madman's Corner* (underwater camera work).